ANNUAL SHOWCASE

Wonderful Wordsmiths

Edited By Bobby Tobolik

First published in Great Britain in 2022 by:

Young Writers
Remus House
Coltsfoot Drive
Peterborough
PE2 9BF
Telephone: 01733 890066
Website: www.youngwriters.co.uk

Printed and bound in the UK by BookPrintingUK
Website: www.bookprintinguk.com
YB0525C

Foreword

Since 1991, here at Young Writers we have celebrated the awesome power of creative writing, especially in children and young adults where it can serve as a vital method of expressing their emotions and views about the world around them.

Usually our creative writing competitions focus on either fiction or poetry in all its forms, but that does leave a gap for other writing skills and styles to fall through. What about all the writing that doesn't fit into either of those categories? Songs and scripts, blogs and book reviews, essays and articles; we wanted to read and celebrate those too! So we created the Annual Showcase, a competition where any style of writing could be submitted up to 1000 words.

Open to all 4-18 year-olds, the Annual Showcase was the perfect opportunity for any budding young writer, or their proud parent or teacher, to submit a piece of writing on any topic and in any style. The extended word limit also allowed these authors to write at length, really exploring their ideas and imagination.

All the entries we've received have been a delight to read. On every topic conceivable, in every style, they prove that these young writers are bursting with ideas and creativity; we just need to give them an outlet! We really hope we've done that with the Annual Showcase, and we hope that you enjoy reading them as much as we have!

Contents

Jake Shayler (11)	188	Olivia Finch (10)	264
Inyana Norris (10)	190	Anjali Ramalingam (7)	265
Summer-Rose Campbell (10)	192	Marni Allcorn (8)	266
Hanan Abdi (11)	194	George Frank Gamble (9)	267
Beatrix Blanco (10)	196	Haasika Vishnuprabhu (9)	268
Omega Lambert-White (9)	198	Oliver Thompson (7)	269
Meghna Boojhowon (7)	201	Fred Gamble (7)	270
Madison Bennett (9)	202	Shakeel Gariba (4)	271
Tamara-Mae Mwandira (8)	204	Joshua Madders (5)	272
Flo Warman (9)	206	Josie Meech (9)	273
Esther Thompson (11)	210	Arun Dutt (5)	274
Lottie Seager (6)	212		
Ruby Muldoon (9)	214		
Eesa Gaffar (10)	216		
Evangeline Ellery (11)	218		
Poppy Langridge (8)	220		
Anna Blazhko (9)	222		
Aditi Sikder (10)	224		
Azra Eva Yavas (11)	226		
Oliver Bayat (9)	228		
Nathan Arnold (9)	230		
Zanna Orunsolu (6)	232		
Rayan Shah (7)	234		
Pola Dworak (9)	236		
Nellie Gustaw (8)	238		
Daisy Northfield (11)	240		
Zoe Da Paixão (10)	242		
Leo Obe (9)	244		
Amina Kanwal (11)	246		
Aarush Garg (11)	248		
Aaron Shaw (5)	250		
Aaryan Acharya	252		
Mia Martin (8)	253		
Tristan Meacher (9)	254		
'Nehita Aigbogun (11)	255		
Meredith Ivy Caunt (6)	256		
Jaafar Aouam (11)	257		
Ethan Lawry (10)	258		
Gifty-Favour Thompson (9)	259		
Kaylan Merrell (11)	260		
Dulcine-Vittoria Dubceac (6)	261		
Ciena Baldwin (11)	262		
Sophia Clayton (11)	263		

THE CREATIVE WRITING

A Forbidden Place Mystery

In a forest far away lived a little girl named Crystal. She lived in the woods with her mum. Do you know why? Well, it's because her father went out hunting, then he suddenly turned around and saw a wolf! He tried to run as fast as he could, but sadly, he didn't make it back alive.

On the 17th of February, Crystal turned ten; she was so excited. When she turned ten, her mother said she could go outside alone, but then Crystal's mum shed tears.

Crystal asked, "Why are you crying?"

Then her mother said, "Darling, you're the only one I have left. So please stay safe. There's a secret I want to tell you; behind this door is all the equipment you need to be successful in life that I saved for you a long time ago." Then her mum said, "When you turn 19, you can open this door."

A while later, when Crystal was figuring out what her mother had said, she heard a noise. She rushed and saw her mum lying down on the floor. Crystal couldn't leave her mum because she was the only family she had left. So she spoke to her mother, but she didn't answer. Crystal was brave; she hoped she would find someone to help her mum, but she couldn't find anyone to help.

Finally, Crystal found a boy. First, he was shy. Then Crystal said hello to the boy and the boy responded. Then they both became friends. Crystal explained everything that had happened to her father and her mum. Finally, Crystal convinced him to go to her house. He agreed and followed her. Suddenly, they turned around to see a wolf behind them. They dashed like they had never before and made it to Crystal's house.

Destiny Onyewuchi (9)

The Lost Backpack

"Where is my backpack?" said Maryum. She headed to her classroom to ask Mr Firwick for help. "Mr Firwick?" asked Maryum.

"Yes?" he said, his deep brown eyes fixed on the paper.

"I've lost my backpack. I've looked everywhere and I can't find it," said Maryum.

"Did you look in your locker?" he replied.

"Yes," said Maryum.

"Have you checked with Principal Lebowski?" he said.

"Yes, but he wasn't there," she said a bit loudly.

"Then check again. Don't come back if he says he can't do anything about it." Mr Firwick was now annoyed and this was Mr Firwick's way of saying go away!

Maryum walked up three levels of stairs then down a long corridor. There was a rough turquoise-coloured carpet. The wall on her right-hand side was grey. The room she was to go in was at the end of the long corridor. She looked at the letters on the big brown door. The letters spelt 'PRIN PAL OFF C' because the letters had fallen off. Maryum gulped and knocked on the door.

"Who is it?" came a squeaky voice from the 'PRIN PAL OFF C'.

"It's me sir, Maryum, remember?" she said back in a squeaky voice.

"Oh no, not again," said the principal under his breath. He waddled to the door, opened it and stared at Maryum disapprovingly.

"Let's go!" said Maryum to Zainab so they headed off.
The next day...

"Finally, Saturday," she said. After, she got dressed. "Now I'm all dressed. I wonder if Mom will make pancakes?" So she headed downstairs and saw her three older brothers downstairs. They looked like her except they were taller.

"You took your time," said Ali, the youngest.

"Zip it," said Maryum.

"No fighting!" said their mother. "Why do you always fight?"

"What's for breakfast, Mom?" said Maryum, ignoring her question.

"I'm making pancakes!"

"Yay!" said Maryum.

After a while Maryum's mom passed out the pancakes.

"Yum," said Maryum, gobbling them down. After breakfast, Maryum reminded her mom that she needed a new backpack.

"Oh, I remember! We'll go to Smiggle after I get changed, okay?" she said, suddenly remembering.

After her mom got dressed, they went to the tram station and went to Smiggle. "Okay dear, which backpack do you like most?" asked her mother once they got there.

"I like the light pink one," she said after looking at all the backpacks.

"Let's get it then."

After they bought it, they went home.

On Monday...

"Guys, look at the new bag my mom bought me!" said Maryum during break time.

"Wow! That's pretty!" said Zainab, looking at the backpack.
"It is!" said Aamira, also looking at it.
"I need to throw my juice box in the dumpster, BRB!" said
Maryum, running off. When she reached the dumpster, she
tried to throw her juice box inside but she missed and it fell
back between the wall and the dumpster. She went to look
for it but while searching for it what did she see? Sitting
beside the juice box was her backpack!
"Are you kidding me?" said Maryum, staring at her
backpack. "I literally just bought a new backpack! I can't
believe this!" she said frustratedly. "All that trouble... for
nothing!" she mumbled as she went back to Aamira and
Zainab.
After school...
"Mom, Mom, I found my backpack!" Maryum said, shouting
as she ran back home to her family.

Zoha Mehdi (10)

The Unknown

It was a warm May evening, and an eleven-year-old girl, named Carla, was playing in her tattered tiny room. She grew up with only a mum who struggled to put food on the table. Carla tried as hard as she could to help. Carla was super smart and had won at least five awards for each and every lesson. She was top in her class and she adored exploring and being an adventurer since she was only two years old. Whenever her teachers were lecturing her class about how everyone but her didn't know the twelve times table, she would sneak outside and solve a mystery! She even once found a unicorn. But time after time, no one ever believed her when she chit-chatted on and on all about mythical creatures.

She has a secret that nobody knows, not even her mum. Carla is a secret agent trying to find, rescue and help extinct creatures. Now, you're probably thinking if they are extinct then you can't save them because they've left and there's none roaming around our planet? Well, here's your answer: she has a time machine so she can go back in time or forwards in time, pretty cool right? But she can't joke because she is on a very special mission to enter The Unknown.

Carla wandered through a strange door that had appeared in her back garden the other morning. She had received a message from her secret spy team that today was the day that she needed to enter The Unknown. Apparently, The Unknown was everything like caves, tombs, even villages and deserts, snowy ice lands and especially a dragon's lair but the thing is where will she go?

Molly Saxton (9)

The Gold Atlantic

Zina Cloud, a nine-year-old girl with long, braided hair, merrily skipped through the glistening snow beside her rosy-cheeked best friend. Zina was wearing long rainbow socks, a luxurious purple gilet and an orange scarf. Whilst wrapping her numb hands in her velvet scarf, Zina stated, "I'm gonna head to the library for my project, you comin'?"

"Yeah sure," replied Fola.

They took a sharp turn down Honeycrust Lane and stared through the frost-covered windows, feeling comforted by the crackling amber fires which were yet so far away. Minutes later, they arrived at the local library and scurried in, hoping for a warm welcoming fire. Zina gingerly strolled across the autumn red rug admiring the ancient books, journals and diaries, which were carpeted with layers of dust.

A group of three were gathered around a chestnut table and talked in hushed voices with serious faces. The person at the far end had colourful streaks in her hair and a star on her forehead. The middle person had pointy ears and glimmering, emerald-green eyes. The person nearest them, who was a boy, had peculiar dragon-like features and burnt lips.

Startled by the pitter-patter of feet, the furthest person swiftly turned around. "Oh, erm, hi," she stuttered. "I'm Myla Silver. This is Cela Clover," she said looking over to the pointy-eared girl. "And that's Theodore Green," she explained.

"Nice to meet you," Fola politely replied, shocked by their unique features.

Zina strolled over to a nearby bookshelf and a gold titled book caught her eye. The spine was wrapped with lush ferns, pink fluffy straw and freshly picked wildflowers. The conversation between Fola, Myla, Cela and Theodore gradually drifted over to Zina's ears.

"Have you seen a book made out of twigs and stuff?" Myla asked.

Zina eagerly replied, "Is this what you're looking for?" She twisted a lock of hair around her finger and impatiently opened the book.

"Noooo!" the three all yelled, lurching forward with worried faces.

Myla's hair suddenly turned multicoloured and the pink star on her forehead took the form of a glimmering pearl-white sculpture.

Cela's nails turned aquamarine and two gossamer shapes formed on her back.

Theodore's large, curious eyes turned a fiery orange and a long vermillion tail slithered down his legs. He opened his mouth to speak but instead, a blast of scorching fire burst out.

Zina and Fola stared in awe, with dinner plate eyes.

Engrossed in all the peculiar transformations, Zina hadn't noticed the black mist carpeting the room.

"Uh-oh, Thyle's been released!" Theo yelled.

They all ran to the park and Myla slowly explained everything that was happening.

"So, we have to put a dark spirit back in this grimoire thingy?" Fola asked.

The grimoire's leaves had started browning and falling off whilst the twigs which bound the book together had started to snap.

"Before the grimoire completely falls apart," added Theo.

Whooosh!

"Argh!" Zina screamed, grabbing Fola's arm.

Theo followed Myla into the tree, situated at the far end of the park. Cela pointed, gesturing them to go first.

Zina carefully stepped into the masterpiece of bark. Colour poured out before them and the aroma of roses and cake led them in. Flamboyant houses drifted along the riverbank and a beautiful canal gave transport through the village.

Snap! A book closed in all the wonders and beauty of Flopa leading them to reality.

"But the pictures were moving?" stuttered Fola, tapping her heel on the concrete.

"Yes, they always do, you just never stare at them long enough to realise," Myla replied in a bossy tone.

Clouds lingered in the air and rain fell to the ground. The once beautiful canal stood frozen in the centre of town. The flourishing houses were now reduced to ashes.

A dark carpet yet familiar to the one in the local library, but far thicker, produced a cruel beauty and snapped at the occasional glare of the sun. "This is the frozen kingdom our village Snugville and Flopa has become," sobbed Myla.

"Well, how do we stop it?" Zina yelled.

"With sunlight," Theo replied. "It's a tricky journey to the gold Atlantic but we can get there by unicorn."

10

"Wait, unicorn?" Zina and Fola exchanged excited glances. Not long after their conversation, they were galloping in the air on top of a magical creature.

A faint glimmer swiftly became a golden lake blazing with sunlight.

"It absorbs 70% of sunlight every day," Cela explained, pulling out five moss balls.

"Dip these in the golden lake and don't drink the water," Mila warned, whilst Theo pretended to lick the moss ball. They flew down to the ground and dipped the moss balls in the silk water. Zina held out her tongue, hoping for an accidental drip of golden water to fall, when a gnome-looking creature, floating on a grey cloud, stole her moss ball.

"Hey! Give it back," Zina ordered.

"Hahaha, do you really think I will give it back? I'm Thyle, the meanie," mocked the gnome.

Zina jumped onto her unicorn and waved Fola to follow. Thyle stealthily followed. The trio weren't so far ahead and soon they were all galloping towards Snugville.

Zina explained their encounter with Thyle but Cela seemed sure they'd succeed with four moss balls.

They landed in the village square and handed the moss to Cela, who flew up and drained the sunlight out of them. Even though they had restored 90% of colour to Flopa, Thyle wasn't going away.

Unexpectedly, a majestic creature, which seemed to have been crafted by a dream, swooped down and blew Thyle away with one flap of his wings. The king.

As Thyle claim closer, he seemed to start burning and eventually fell off his cloud and was caught in the grimoire, by Fola.
Every raindrop of sunlight restored light to Flopa and soon everyone was happily chitter-chattering inside, serving plates of mouth-watering jelly, doughnuts and cookies.

Misha Aisha Siddiqui (10)

The European Adventure

I still haven't forgotten when I went on a trip from England to Bulgaria which lasted 45 hours. First things first, I woke up early in the morning, got ready and got in the car so we could drive to the ferry boat.

When we arrived in Dover, which is a city, we got a ferry boat because in part of the city you can get a ferry boat. When I went on the ferry, I felt like I was in a mall because there was a shop, a restaurant, a smoking area, an outside area, the main area and lots more. There were three levels on the ferry and we went on all of them with enjoyment. When the ferry boat arrived in France, we went to the lower ground, got our car and drove out of the ferry.

After half an hour, we drove out of France and arrived in Belgium. We stopped to eat at Burger King and drove around Belgium for four hours until we drove out of Belgium and went into Germany.

In Germany, we passed Berlin and we drove around Germany for eight hours. When we drove out of Germany, we drove to Austria and we stopped at a very fun park which also had benches and tables, there was even an alpine. We drove around Austria for six hours until we drove out of Austria and arrived in Hungary.

In Hungary, we just stopped a few times to buy some food and we drove around for three hours. When we came out of Hungary, we went to Slovenia and in Slovenia, we pretty much did the same things we did in Hungary. We stayed in Slovenia for two hours and after Slovenia, we went to Serbia.

Nesha Angelova

The Raiders' Rebellion

Cynthia stared dully through the orphanage window at the same sunrise and rippling blue sea that she'd seen for the past six years. She registered dimly that it was her fourteenth birthday, but she brushed the thought away with a sigh. It was another stark reminder of the day she lost everything she knew and loved, before being shoved into a filthy shack that she'd been forced to call home ever since. Just then, the morning bell rang. Cynthia leapt up and ran downstairs almost robotically. She was first to the breakfast table, apart from the scowling matron. Orphans slowly trickled into the room while she devoured her pitiful meal. There was hardly any noise, just chewing and the rustle of Matron's newspaper. Cynthia, always daring, asked, "Anything interesting in the paper, ma'am?" The others looked up, excited to see the consequences.

Matron glared at her, before grumbling, "Not that it's any of your business, but the Raiders may be returning."

A collective gasp reverberated around the room. Cynthia flinched as though she'd been slapped. The Raiders? Again? Surely not, there couldn't be a repeat of what happened last time... Cynthia could still vividly remember what had happened on that fateful day. They had mercilessly plundered every home in the vicinity, leaving no one alive to tell the tale. The table sat in complete silence, all dreading and contemplating their futures.

Later, the chef, Mollie, called out, "Cynthia, darling, could you get me some groceries?" Mollie had a soft spot for the girl, usually entrusting her with tasks.

Cynthia absent-mindedly nodded and was then shunted outside. She pocketed the shopping list, then set off to the market. The usual hubbub in the streets was an eerie quiet. When going to purchase the chef's ingredients, she suddenly heard a hasty mutter between two passers-by: "Yes, I've heard about the rebellion against the Raiders. I'm doing what I can to help, what about you?"

Abandoning all other tasks immediately, Cynthia marched up to the men and declared confidently, "I overheard you. And I want in." The adults exchanged uneasy looks at this, clearly unsure why a teenager was so interested in their conversation, not to mention the fact that she was flaunting such suspicious behaviour.

The older one of the pair narrowed his eyebrows and gruffly said, "We aren't talking about stuff for little kids. Move along now, there's a good girl."

Unable to stand their patronising looks, she glared at them. "I'm serious! I lost everything to those vile robbers, it's about time they got their comeuppance!"

He opened his mouth to protest but was cut off by his partner. "Ah, let her join, you can't stop her. She looks old enough to me."

The stubborn teenager smirked. They handed her a scrap of paper, before stalking off. It read: 'Tonight in the market at 11. Be there.' She memorised it, then returned to the orphanage with a bag of fresh produce and a satisfied smile.

The usually boisterous children were reduced to quiet mice, much to Cynthia's relief. Everyone did as they were told, no fuss whatsoever. It made her plan quite simple. At night, everyone slowed drifted off, while Cynthia, tossed and turned, completely restless, waiting for the distinct sound of Matron's snores.

She waited in agonising silence, but eventually, she heard the noise she'd waited for. Careful not to raise an alarm, she dressed and crept downstairs, cautiously avoiding the creaking stairs that would spell disaster for her. Eventually, she made it to the door, then slipped out without another word.

Surprisingly, the marketplace was extremely crowded, albeit quiet; it looked like half the population had turned up. Even though she'd signed up for it, she had to admit to herself that she felt uneasy being there. A sinister atmosphere hung low upon all of them, no matter how much they tried to turn a blind eye to it.

The citizens kept arriving for a while, before a man stepped onto a podium, calling for silence. "Listen up, everyone. You know what you've signed up for, and I commend each and every one of you. We are here to get justice for everything we went through six years ago, to take back what is rightfully ours from the Raiders!"

A huge cheer reverberated throughout the marketplace. The leader smiled, then said, "You all know what to do. Hurry in your plans, however, because we have less than a day before our courage is put to the test!"

Everyone broke into groups and began scheming excitedly. Unsure what to do, Cynthia slid into the nearest group. A woman was handing out various tools, saying, "As you all know, we're going to be part of the front attackers. I got these, and they should work as weapons if we..." Cynthia stopped paying attention; she was thrilled. The front attackers! It sounded incredibly important (and dangerous, but she paid no attention to that). She found a sharp rake being thrust at her, and at that moment, the reality of it sunk in. *Yes, it's going to happen*, she thought to herself, *and I want to be there when it does.*

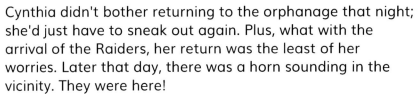

Cynthia didn't bother returning to the orphanage that night; she'd just have to sneak out again. Plus, what with the arrival of the Raiders, her return was the least of her worries. Later that day, there was a horn sounding in the vicinity. They were here!

With a loud cry, the townspeople charged forward and caught the plunderers off guard. They yelped, seeing that fighting back was no use, grabbed what they could and immediately dropped it with the threat of being stabbed violently, before running for their lives. Few made it through and the rest were captured with ease.

A cheer swept through the crowd and Cynthia was almost skipping back to the orphanage. Matron would kill her, she thought, but it didn't matter. Nothing mattered compared to the true happiness she felt at that very moment.

Anika Gulati (11)

The Zoo

Whilst the cotton-candy clouds zoomed across the azure sapphire sky, class 3A got ready for their most awaited trip of the year. Their antiquated, rickety coach was getting the final tweaks to make sure it wouldn't break down halfway through the journey. Eagerly, the children hopped onto the bus and sat down, giggling and chattering.

"Quiet!" Miss Tingle barked as she entered the coach, her eyelashes fluttering maliciously. Abruptly, it became silent. So silent you could hear a pin drop. Since she was the assistant teacher of class 3A, it was mandatory for her to come on every school trip. Being the scariest teacher of the school, she would give children hours upon hours of detention for the tiniest of things. When she entered a room, lightning struck. Every child would make sure they were doing the right thing, including no talking, no slouching, girls sitting ladylike and much more. The teachers' excuse was that she lived in solitude and was old-school. However, the children didn't believe a word. Well, Lilah didn't. Not one percent.

"Okay, let's settle down, children." The coach exploded with positive energy once Mr White, their science teacher, entered. His happy-to-help attitude spread smiles everywhere. He was Lilah's favourite teacher. He signalled to the driver to start driving and in a few minutes' time, they had left the school premises to go to the zoo.

Rumbling and rolling, the van continued to hobble along like an old lady. Sometimes, Lilah would resemble the school van to Miss Tingle, old and disgusting but still working. Lilah had many questions about Miss Tingle. Why is she not retired? Does she have relatives? Why is she a Miss not a Mrs? Lilah knew the answer to that. It was because she was a horrid witch. As ugly as a frog. No one would marry her.

An hour later, class 3A arrived at the renowned London Zoo. The children excitedly cheered.

"Remember to stay in your pairs and listen to Mrs Tingle and me at all times," Mr White announced once they entered the zoo.

"And NO misbehaviour," Miss Tingle sneered, her crooked nose up high. With that said, 3A continued on their tour. During the morning, they spotted parrots, pandas and even lions! When lunch came, 3A chose to sit outside, next to the chimpanzees. Lilah had a sandwich and her mum's homemade banana bread. She gobbled up her sandwiches rapidly so she could savour her banana bread. It smelt amazing, especially since Lilah's mum used a floral essence only available in UAE - her home country.

The aromatic essence pervaded the chimpanzees' habitat. As she savoured bite after bite, the huge, soft, cinnamon-brown banana bread's smell became more and more distinct. Lilah's sixth sense told her to stop, but the delectable monstrosity had taken over. At this point, Lilah could barely hear the stifled voice of everybody. The taste of the bread was like a flower in her mouth, hypnotising her. Her eyes began to droop until she was awoken by a deafening screech.

19

"AAAAAHHHHH! Chimpanzees on the loose!" Miss Tingle screamed.

At that point, Lilah realised two things: one was that Miss Tingle could scream like a crow, and two, which was more important, chimpanzees were out! Before she could acknowledge it, the greedy chimpanzees had already hunted the aroma and were charging towards her.

She could hear her best friend Mia shouting her lungs out. "Lilah, let go of the bread! Let go of the bread!" Lilah shook her head. "You have to! The zookeeper said their nails were cut last month and are too long. You'll get cut!"

Lilah didn't want to leave the bread. There had to be another way. However, there wasn't any time. Reluctantly, she tossed the bread near the chimpanzees' cage and ran as fast as her short legs could carry her. Her mouth watered seeing the chimpanzees gnawing on the bread. Still, she was delighted that she threw it. She could hear and see the chimpanzees' nails scraping on the floor like chalkboards. If she hadn't let go, Lilah would have gone to the hospital; or worse, she could've kicked the bucket!

"Now that was close," she sighed, sitting down with relief.

"Lilah, are you seeing what I'm seeing?" Mia asked, pointing at Miss Tingle. Once Lilah saw it, she pinched herself. She blinked a million times until she realised it was real - Miss Tingle was transforming into a monster!

Lilah gawped whilst Miss Tingle's hair turned into scales, her mouth into a beak, fingers into talons and dragon wings appeared on her back. Miss Tingle wasn't human; she was a beast!

"Stay back!" Lilah turned backwards to see Mr White running towards the beast, a rod in his hand. He was running millions of miles an hour. He was too quick for the dragon-like creature and chopped its wings off so it couldn't fly. Steam billowed out of her ears and her scaly face wrinkled in pain. Its next reaction was a talon swipe. It missed drastically. It was blind!

"Mr White! It's blind, you can lure it away!" Lilah told Mr White.

He yelled at the beast. It listened and came rampaging to him.

Behind Mr White, everyone was holding nets. Not one, not two, not even three. There were ten for they didn't know how fierce the creature was. When the vile animal was close to Mr White, he glided to the side.

Roaring and screaming, the beast tore the first and second nets. Then the third, then the fourth. The air became humid. The wind howled. The sun hid behind the shivering clouds. Lilah began to worry - was her plan going to work? Then, the beast slowed down and at the sixth net, it halted. The zookeepers tied it up. Police sirens blared and soon, policemen chained the beast up and took it away with a struggle.

What a day! In all their life, class 3A won't see something as crazy as what happened that day in the zoo.

Sabeeqa Syed (11)

Desert Island Discovery

It was a beautiful, sunny morning. The scorching, golden sunshine beamed brightly above them. The fluffy, pink-white clouds drifted calmly like a sleeping baby. Above them, the sky was as blue as the sapphire-blue sea.

Mary and Daisy were on holiday with their dad, John. Mary was twelve years old. She had walnut-brown, wavy hair tied in a plait, hanging like a rope. Her wide jade eyes twinkled with laughter. Her rosy-plum cheeks were like juicy tomatoes. The yellow sleeveless dress that she wore swayed joyously as she skipped along with her little sister.

Daisy was the six-year-old sister whose emerald-green eyes were like saucers full of naughtiness. Her golden-brown, silky hair danced about as she jumped excitedly. She had a crimson-raspberry maxi dress that swished like the sea waves.

Their dad John - dressed in aqua-green shorts and a mellow yellow shirt - towered above the children. His spikey, chestnut-brown hair appeared like a hedgehog sitting on his head and his royal-blue eyes were as deep as the deep blue sea. He grinned as he watched his daughters singing and going round and round him like a merry-go-round. He was getting their boat ready for their planned journey. "Alright, girls, let's get going."

Holding hands, Mary and Daisy darted towards their red, wooden boat while Dad pushed it out into the water and jumped in. "All aboard!" they chorused enthusiastically as they sailed out into the deep, crystal-blue sea.

Mary lifted her black binoculars to closely view the beautiful island ahead. She noticed the craggy, colossal cliffs curving cheerfully like a roller coaster in the sky. The soft, green grass glistened glamorously like a blanket of emeralds.

John took a deep breath of the balmy fresh air. The seagulls squawked noisily in the air like needles piercing through their ears. Daisy held her nose as she smelt stinky seaweed around her. She could also taste the fish in the salty air. The gentle breeze tickled them as the boat bobbed like a bouncing ball playfully in the water.

When the island finally came into view, John steered their boat towards the island. As soon as he tied it to the buoy, Mary jumped out excitedly and felt the hot grainy sand slipping and sliding on her toes. Daisy followed Mary and raced merrily to the cold sea. Immediately, they began to build sandcastles and played with the cream-bronze shells that dotted about the honey-gold sand. The pistachio-green lush trees swayed gently in the cool breeze.

Later on, the girls played hide-and-seek with their chirpy laughter echoing on the island. Soon, they began to sweat in the golden, scorching sunshine. The frothy waves of the turquoise-blue sea lapped on the shore, inviting them to have a delicious swim. As they cooled themselves off, they noticed the rainbow-coloured corals resting like sleeping sculptures under the waves while fiery-red fish flapped their fins furiously.

After a while, they all began to feel hungry. Suddenly, they realised they had no food! Their tummies were rumbling like thunderclouds. John was wide-eyed in shock (how could he forget to bring food?) and the girls began to lick their lips. They looked up at their father with questioning eyes. John soon realised he would have to hunt for food. Tears like dripping rain rolled down Daisy's cheeks and Mary's lips drooped like weeping willows. This seemed hard to them.

Fortunately, John spotted a green palm tree in the distance full of juicy, brown coconuts hanging like baubles. Eureka! His eyes dazzled like bright-lit stars. He grinned from ear to ear. "Not to worry, girls. Daddy to the rescue." Speedily, he dashed towards the towering palm tree.

Quickly, like little lambs, the girls followed their dad. Filled with delight, John climbed up the tree cautiously, while Mary waited anxiously but Daisy stamped her feet impatiently on the ground.

A little later, John plucked three, huge, juicy, chocolate-brown coconuts. All in all, the trio gobbled up their hearty meal like hungry hyenas! Daisy collected the empty coconut shells to take them back home. Mary spotted a bottle cork washed up by the sea. The girls played ping-pong with twigs and the cork.

Exhausted by then, the family headed back wearily to their boat and flopped like dead fish. Daisy rubbed her sunken eyes that were like heavy cannon balls and yawned sleepily. Mary dragged her tired legs and crawled slowly like a snail. John's shoulders slouched like a heavy sack as he stretched his legs out in the boat. With big yawns and heads as hot as fire, they slumped down on the boat sleepily. They all watched the spectacular evening, golden-red sun setting in the horizon. It was time to go back.

As they drifted calmly back towards their home, all of a sudden, their feet were in a carpet of cold water. *Glug, glug, glug!* "OH NO!" John buried his face in his hands while the girls began to bite their fingers. A cork-sized hole winked wickedly at them. In no time, the boat began to capsize.

The girls screeched like gulls and all of them turned as pale as ghosts. With his heart pounding like a hammer, John desperately started to search for something to block the hole.

Like a lightning flash, Mary recalled she had a cork in her pocket. "Will this be of any help?" She held it out for John to see, who without further delay popped it urgently in the hole. Daisy offered some pieces of the coconut shell she had saved and together with Mary, they stamped the cork and the shell in the hole.

With butterflies in their tummies and jittery nerves, they all scooped the water out of the boat with left-over coconut shells. Relieved, the family once again settled down calmly. John, Mary and Daisy huddled together and waited. The cool sea breeze lulled them to a sound sleep until they finally reached home.

Nazia Gangjee (6)

A Magical Mission

I arrived at the secret meeting place, where a wizard was telling everyone their missions. My mission was to go to a magical valley. A guard appeared to try and stop me from doing my mission. I defeated the guard and went through the golden gates. The place looked mysterious and ancient. I was surprised to find natural artefacts. I had to solve a riddle before I could pick anything up, if I didn't, the gates would shut and I would have tripped the alarm so that the building collapsed. Thankfully, I solved the riddle and grabbed a few pieces.

"I can't believe I'm still alive!" I squealed.

After my heart had slowed down, I started to walk back to the gates.

"Hopefully the guard has gone by now," I said to myself.

In the distance, a dark silhouette caught my attention...

"Wait! Is that the guard? This can't be!" I shouted, in disbelief. "I really thought he was gone."

What if I never get back? I started to doubt myself. I started to cry. "I'm never going to make it back!" I wailed.

I suddenly snapped back to reality. "This is all nonsense," I objected, trying to reassure myself.

I quickly wiped my tears and continued walking.

A few minutes later, I finally reached the gates. "Time to fight this guard, I guess."

I snuck up behind him, getting ready to strike, when I realised... "He's a mannequin?"

I couldn't believe it! This meant I could slip through the gates without being stopped. I questioned my decision. *He was here earlier. I just don't understand.*

I decided not to overthink it. I was just about to slip through the gates when the guard appeared out of nowhere. He had caught me in the act...

"Well, well, well, if it isn't little miss, you," he said in a menacing tone.

"Oh no!"

"You haven't defeated me yet," he smirked, slyly.

I was going to make a run for it. I had to. I turned my head before hearing, "Don't, even, think about it!" he barked, now in a stern tone.

I ignored him and ran. Ran like my life was depending on it. Because it was...

After running for miles, I managed to finally outrun him. I wanted to see the wealthy treasures I had grabbed, so I walked into a dark, gloomy alleyway, which had graffiti on its walls, trying not to look suspicious.

Once I was in a quiet, isolated corner, I unpacked my heavy bag and stared in awe as I saw all the jewels sparkle and glow in the twilight sky.

Later on, I arrived back at the secret meeting place. I was told to put the jewels in a compartment, which was in the passcode-locked lab, upstairs. Before I put away the jewels, I grabbed a few diamonds to keep. I was planning to put them up for auction. I'm hoping to get a lot of money for them.

Mission #2...

Online, I found out diamonds sold for a lot, but it said it mainly mattered how ancient the diamond was. Since I had finished my first mission, I was allowed the day off. I already knew what I'd spend my time on... It's auctioning time!

At the auctioning grounds, I was looking forward to my profit. It was time to start the bidding process. The auctioneer carefully examined each and every item that was being auctioned that day. I don't know why but she made thorough checks of my diamonds before declaring, "These are fakes!"

The crowd had a ripple of shock. I was shocked too. I even gasped myself even though I knew this was going to happen. Nobody ever got past the auctioneer with diamonds. Everyone thinks that only royalty can have or find diamonds and bring them here. I decided to stand up for myself.

"Excuse me?" I muttered politely.

"Yes?" came the reply.

She located where the sound was coming from and beckoned me to stand up. Even though I didn't want to, I did as I was told.

"So, what do you want?"

"I want the chance to explain the truth about those diamonds!" I answered firmly.

The crowd laughed. I felt so embarrassed. The lady saw how awkward I was, so she decided to give me a chance. The lady hushed the crowd and spoke. "Five minutes max," she told me.

"It's a long story b..." I started.

She interrupted me. "Five minutes!" she reminded me, making sure she repeated it at least twice.

"As I was saying, it's a long story but I am willing to shorten it down for you," I continued with lots of enthusiasm.

I was very frustrated and annoyed that she interrupted me. "Basically, what happened is I was told to retrieve artefacts which were in a temple. When I got there, I solved the riddle to get the artefacts and thankfully didn't trip the alarm." She started to rapidly fire questions at me. "Then why didn't you take the artefacts back?"

"I did," I answered.

"Why are they here then?" she continued.

"I was allowed to keep a few," I lied.

I felt like I was in court. There was an awkward silence...

"I still don't believe you," came a voice from the silence. It was the lady.

"Get out!" she barked, while banging her hammer. "And take your fakes with you!"

I couldn't believe my ears. I was willing to protest for this... and I did.

A couple of weeks later, I finally had a group of people agreeing with me. We stormed into the auctioning grounds and managed to get our rights. I got my money and I was extremely joyful! Even though the lab found out, it was still worth it. I gave them 25% of the money so I wouldn't get fired! I was left with a whopping 175 grand! A trip to Hawaii it is!

Nicole Abitimo Oloya (10)

The Diary Of An Evacuee

My name is Maisie Smith. I am eleven years old. It is the 30th of August 1939. This is my story.

The day started like any other normal Wednesday. We awoke at 7:30am and had breakfast but instead of Mother walking us to school, she took us to the town hall where men dressed in army uniforms handed out gas masks. We tried them on and looked like scary aliens!

The strange behaviour continued the following day with Mother and Father acting oddly. They bought us presents we didn't need and barely had the money for; little dolls for my younger sisters, Rosie and Lillie, and for me, a journal with a key.

The next morning, we were awoken early by Mother. In the corner were three suitcases, neatly packed and labelled. She washed our hair with her own special shampoo and lavender soap, even though we usually used carbolic which made our eyes sting. She dressed us in our Sundays and tied our plaits with white silky ribbons.

"Time to go now, little darlings. Oh, I'll miss you so!" She started crying, and it made me worry. How was she going to look after herself if we weren't there to comfort her?

After our last hugs, Mother pulled me aside and said, "Look after your sisters, dear. They're in your hands now. See you soon."

We boarded the train and found our seats. Rosie started to cry, and Lillie let out the occasional sniffle. I remembered something Mother used to say. "There there, chin up, chickens. Any cheeps?"

They cheeped obediently. Thinking of Mother was a mistake as I too found tears in my eyes. "No Maisie, you can't cry. You must be a brave girl and look after the girls," I said this quietly to myself to make sure no one else heard.

Our schoolteacher, Miss Allen, had travelled with us. "Gather your things, children, and follow me to the town hall where your new countryside families will meet you," she said.

We entered the hall and sat on the floor obediently. A couple with a baby bouncing on the mother's hip and a little girl holding her hand walked over to us. "We'll take you two," the mother proclaimed, pointing at Rosie and Lillie.

I tugged on Lillie's arm and whispered, "Look out for Rosie, okay? Be brave, Lillie, be brave."

A couple with a mean expression on their faces came over to me. "Come on, grab your things. Chop chop!" the father barked.

I grabbed my belongings and we walked to a big, black house. I slept in a dark attic room, on a rusty iron bed with just a thin, worn blanket to keep me warm.

My days were spent cooking and cleaning for Mr and Mrs Harrison and generally being a skivvy for them. My nights were spent dreaming about seeing my family again.

One miserable Wednesday afternoon, after I took a break from endless work for one minute to catch my breath, I heard footsteps and jolted back into action. "There's been a bombing in Guildford. That's where you're from isn't it, girl?" sneered Mr Harrison, then without a further word, he walked off.

That night, I was restless. I kept worrying about my parents; what had happened? I knew what had to be done. I carefully climbed out of bed, pulled on my jumper, skirt, and shoes, and was on my way.

I had never walked the streets alone before, let alone after dark, but I knew I had to, for Father, for Mother. I wearily walked the five miles to the station and when the train arrived, I jumped on board without the guard seeing me. When I arrived at Guildford, it was almost midnight, and I made my way to the hospital where I found the reception desk. "Excuse me, do you have any patients named William and Laura Smith? If you please, nurse, my parents are patients here and I simply must see them."

"Do you know what time it is?" she snapped. "We don't allow children on the ward unless they're patients, and certainly not at this time. But bad luck, girl, they're not here. Perhaps this will teach you to not disturb your elders and betters at extraordinary hours. Now, be off with you!"

All that was left for me to do now was head back home, to my real home, not the Harrisons'.

A few hours later I was finally there, but it looked strangely different now. Where were our neighbours' houses? Where was the greengrocer's? Our street had clearly borne the brunt of the Blitz, but had our house survived? As I traipsed through the rubble and destruction of the bombings, there in the distance was the ruins of a house that stood surrounded by rubble and looked worryingly like mine. As I approached, my worst fears were realised - it was my house. But if my house had been destroyed, what of my parents? Where were they when the bombs hit?

Slowly the front door creaked open then fell off its hinges, revealing a dirty, blood-stained hand and arm where the doorknob once was. Attached to the hand was a small gold watch that I remember seeing when I was here last. That watch belonged to my father, and it was he who cautiously peered through the open doorframe.

32

"Father!" I shouted in jubilation, and with no hesitation ran over the debris into his welcoming arms. I felt another pair of arms around me, crushing me with emotion and realised Mother was there too.

Behind them appeared Lillie and Rosie who joined in the tearful reunion and for what seemed like an eternity, we held onto each other, desperate to not let the embrace ever end. Finally, with tear-stained faces, we looked, first at each other, then at the ruins of our beautiful house.

I realised that we weren't just going to have to rebuild our home, we would have to rebuild our entire lives too.

Orla Hamilton (9)

Alex And The Crown

Chapter 1 - The Attack

In a land far, far away, where everything was blocks, there lived a girl called Alex and her friends Steve, Nick, Ash and Crack, but don't forget about Oinky their pet pig. They lived in a network of trees and underwater houses. One day a shiny, purple portal opened in the sky. Suddenly there was a mighty roar and thousands of Endermen teleported to the ground. Then the almighty Ender Dragon came.

Alex's mother said, "You and your friends go to the underground bunker until the danger is over."

Alex and her friends heard terrible rumbles. When the danger was over, Alex rushed off to find her mother. She found her but NOOOOOOO she was slowly dying. With her last breath, she said, "Find the crown."

Nick said, "Alex, how are we supposed to find the crown?"

"Well, let's start by going into the portal."

Chapter 2 - The Wither

Alex and her friends found themselves in another world where everything was black, grey and red. Suddenly a piggy sort of creature appeared and started to attack them with a golden sword and then more came. They were outnumbered 11 to 6 (if you count their pet pig).

Ash said, "They don't look friendly if you ask me!"

"Look behind us!" said Steve. There was a forest gleaming like an emerald.

They ran into the forest and saw a castle, then saw they had no choice but to climb up it. No sooner had they arrived, they realised it was filled with mobs!

They did not see creepers or zombies, they saw skeletons with swords. The skeletons started to hit them so they ran around the castle but found a dead end.

They hit until the skeletons were defeated and what did they leave behind? A Netherite sword! Crack picked it up and gave it to Alex and they made camp.

The next day they were awoken by a white, floating monster. They scrambled into the centre of the Nether castle as they thought they would be safe there. But no, right ahead of them was a black-brown, slimy creature.

Alex started to hit the creature with her sword but after two hits it split into two creatures! After four hits, it split into four creatures and after eight, there were eight creatures! Alex found and killed seven but where was the eighth? Alex and her friends looked behind blocks and in caves but shouldn't have done because the cave was home to piglins! Suddenly an almighty wither arose and dropped bombs on the piglins. Alex and her friends hid until the battle was over. They stared in amazement at all the crossbows and golden swords the creatures dropped and at the far end, where the wither was, there was one obsidian block, flint and steel, one Netherite sword and three wither skulls. They all rushed to collect as many things as possible.

They ran back to the glowing forest and there, they made a fortress surrounded by a moat of lava. It ran right around the treehouse.

Nick asked, "How are we supposed to cross the moat?"

"We're not," said Alex, "but the striders are. Striders live in pens so if we make a pen then they will all come to us."

Suddenly Oinky started to jump up and down. The friends followed the pig to the edge of the moat and Alex said, "What is it, Oinky, what is it?" Alex looked up and saw an army of floating yellow monsters on the other side of the moat.

Chapter 3 - The Battles

The monsters dug a tunnel under the moat of lava. It took a while so Alex and her friends hopped on the striders and headed towards the castle. When they got there, they were hit by wither skeletons so they used their crossbows and swords to fight them off. As Alex and her friends hadn't ventured far into the gloomy castle walls, they decided to take a closer look inside but as they did, they heard a strange crackling noise. It was just around the corner from them! At the bend of the corner, they realised they shouldn't have ventured in because what they saw was worse than any mob in history. It was a mob spawner and it was spawning piglins! The piglins saw them and started to attack. Alex thought fast and shouted, "If we put some of our armour on they won't attack us!" So they did as Alex suggested and one by one, the piglins started to walk away. "Hooray!" shouted Alex but right in their path was a floating yellow creature. It hovered just above the ground, spinning flaming torches around itself.

Alex and her friends took a step back. Alex felt like there was something important on the other side of the creature. The crew decided that they wanted to take it down so they pushed through and defeated the flaming beast and on the other side they saw the crown! Steve rushed to grab it but there was a sudden click. Ash knew that Steve had stepped on a pressure plate and lava was going to spurt out of a dispenser. Nick and Crack shouted, "RUN!"

Steve did as he was told and ran as fast as his little rectangular legs would carry him! Just as the lava was closing in on him, he made it back to the team where they all had to put their square heads together to make a plan. After a while, Nick said, "I've got it! Let's make a bridge of blocks over the lava."

"It's worth a try!" exclaimed Steve. So the team began to collect and place blocks made of strong obsidian.

When they had completed the bridge, they all took a step back and Steve said, "That looks perfect." Everyone agreed and made their way to the other side. They opened a huge door and saw the crown! The team decided that Alex should have it for her cunning, bravery and courage.

Tom Wadsworth (7)

The Wolves Of Smoke

"The alchemists lived a big life filled with happiness. The End," finished Uncle Igor.

"Just one more, pllleeaase," the three children begged.

"Okay, settle down. The Legend of the Wolves of Smoke."

"A long time ago there was a beautiful and kind woman. Her parents had loved her so much they had given her the name Mila which meant 'loved by the people.' She had a wonderful life as the daughter of the rulers of Russia. One tragic night, her parents were murdered; many people found their strategic and smart ways of leading unfair and thought they gave the richer folk more privileges. The rest of her childhood was spent locked in a tower as her father's cruel brother took control and convinced the people his nasty ways of ruling were for the best. Unfortunately, until Mila became eighteen, she had no right to do anything but watch helplessly. Once she came of age, her uncle was imprisoned, and she became the ruler. Sadly, after all the horrors she had been through it now reflected on her. She became a selfish leader and was known by her second name, Empress Kira, which meant 'leader of the people.' She eventually learned to be a sorceress and immortalised some wolves which were then known as shadow wolves. To this day she is said to roam the snowy lands of Russia, claiming the souls of innocent people who have got lost in the harsh wasteland, and making them her shadow servants. The End."

"Goodnight, Uncle Igor," the children chorused.

"Goodnight, little cubs."

Chapter 1
Me and my little brother raced across the grounds, powdery snow crunching beneath our threadbare shoes. The guards gazed at us with suspicious eyes. My stomach tightened at the sight of the lunch queue. Hopefully, we could find some friends nearer the front who'd let us squeeze in.
We trudged along at the back, rubbing our hands together and stamping our feet. Once we reached the front, our bowls were filled halfway, which in my opinion was half empty, not half full, with brown sludge. Many rumours had gone around about the food in the camp, like, one said they found a rat's tail. Another said that they saw Cook spit in a bowl to clean it. My brother Sergei choked on something and when we finally got it out it appeared to be a bolt.

Chapter 2
I had lived in Moscow for seven years before me, Papa and Mama (who was pregnant) were taken to our leader's (Stalin) horribly cruel camp.
Soon after we arrived there, my brother was born, and Mama became ill.
I made a friend called Uncle Igor, who read me and the other two children on the camp a story every night.
When I was ten, Papa died, his lungs weren't working properly after non-stop labouring in the mine for three years. Me and my brother became orphans a year later because of the illness that had afflicted Mama for four years.

Uncle Igor was old but cared for us and took us in like we were his own. Six months later, he was also gone. And so me and Sergei were on our own in the world, along with the other children, Mikhail and Ivan. Only Ivan had his babushka and Mikhail had his older brother and mama.

Chapter 3

That night my home called for me, the city where I grew up was still there waiting for me. A plan started unfolding in my brain. Escape. There was one danger that kept coming back to me. The wolves of smoke. So many people had attempted to escape, and so many had failed. Either they had been caught, they had been consumed by the cold or, for most, the wolves had found them and Empress Kira had claimed their souls.

If you were out in the wasteland and you heard them, you would run and most likely hear the bloodthirsty hounds right behind you. People said when you turned to look at them all you saw was the land you'd covered. Even when they were so close you could feel their breath, there was nothing but icy snow.

But I felt strong, bold and brave. Nothing could stop me now! And one thing that pushed me on was something Papa told me when we were taken from our home. He said, "Look at me, Natalya, listen. I know you're scared. I want you to make sure you always know how great you are, never give up. Okay, can you do that for me because I might not always be here to make sure you do it? Promise?"

"Yes."

"Also make sure you die knowing you're free, outside these walls."

Chapter 4

After lunch, all of us children found each other while sweeping the snow off the slippery paths, which we had planned. "We need to talk. Come on, it needs to be private." With that, I tugged my friends.

Together we went to our only secret place, behind a huge snowbank, next to one of the sleeping shacks. We pulled our grey overalls tighter around our shoulders as the cold wind picked up.

"So what is it, Natalya?" Mikhail asked.

"Well, do you like it here? Honestly?" I questioned.

"Nah, course not, Tally," he replied.

"Yeah, why would we?" asked Ivan.

The coldness gripped my insides tight, and I tugged Sergei closer, his cold body pressed against mine.

"Exactly, you wouldn't. I... Well... I want to escape!" I could feel my cheeks buzzing at the thought.

"Nope."

"No way."

Hours of convincing later, we had begun to plan to put this vile place behind us. I was dying to show Sergei, who was now six, what the world was like beyond the camp. I remembered the plants and the laughter, the fun and joy and love and freedom, the happiness on every face as they walked through the most beautiful city in the world and my home. Moscow.

Juno Mettam (11)

Flashing Numbers At Highmouth Primary

My story begins in the back of my family's black shiny car on the way to my new school, Highmouth Primary. I was dreading the first day, in the fear I wouldn't fit in.

I had a special power called autism which makes my brain work differently which might make me faster at solving puzzles or codes for example. Although I was not proud of it as I should be, I just wanted to be normal.

When the car stopped, I sighed, seized my bags, and reluctantly clambered out of the car. My parents wished me good luck and I waved them goodbye, turning to face the ominously looming school gates. I gulped and then slowly walked in. The school was as big as I imagined, with high stone walls and multiple rooms.

A cold hand tapped me on the shoulder. I jumped and slowly turned round, there was a tall man standing next to me. He had dark green eyes, long black hair and was enveloped in a dark cloak. "Why are you gawping, boy!" the man spat.

I quickly shut my mouth. "I was just trying to find the Year 5 classroom, sir," I said.

The intimidating figure indicated a finger to a brown door saying 'Yr 5'.

"Thank you," I said quaveringly.

Once through the door, I met a long winding staircase, and I climbed up, bag dragging along the floor. When I finally reached the top, I turned right to find another brown door saying 'Yr 5'. I quickly found my peg and put my school bag on it. Then I turned the silver door handle and walked in.

Instantly the whole class turned their heads. Mrs Falcott, my teacher, a tall lady with long brown hair and soft brown eyes, welcomed me. "Hello," she said in a kind, warm voice. "Year 5, this is Arthur Bradford. I would like you to welcome him and say hello."

"Hello," the class echoed. Mrs Falcott pointed to a table of four with three pupils sitting around it.

"Sit down there, darling," she said helpfully. "Charlie, you will be Arthur's buddy."

A nice-looking boy turned round, he had brown curly hair and bright blue eyes. "Hallo," said Charlie, as I sat down next to him.

"Hi," I greeted him, a little nervously.

"Have you got any questions?" Charlie asked.

"Yes, one," I said. I was starting to like Charlie. "When do lessons start?" This wasn't a stupid question as the children were all chatting loudly.

"Nine on the dot," answered Charlie.

A few minutes later I heard the clock chime. I counted them. 1... 2... 3... 4... 5... 6... 7... 8... 9, nine chimes. Lessons were beginning...

"Turn right." Charlie steered me down a narrow corridor. "Now turn left into the lunch hall."

I felt overwhelmed by how many people were in the great hall, all bustling and jostling to get to the front of the queue. Suddenly a loud voice boomed out, "Single file!" The same man that had spat at me in the morning was striding towards the crowd of pupils. All the children hastily formed a single file line. This man was obviously well known.

"Who's that?" I whispered to Charlie.

"That's Mr Kowalski, he teaches Year Six, but everyone knows he's angling to be headmaster," Charlie whispered back.

I gulped.

At long last, we finally had lunch, sausage casserole it turned out, and jam doughnuts for pudding.

When the pupils lined up after lunch break, I saw a girl out of the corner of my eye dart through the line and back into the courtyard. Charlie said it was probably Luna, and she was just going to fill up her bottle. Apparently, she always did that.

When we were back up in the classroom, doing symmetry, which we had been doing for half an hour, Luna still wasn't back. Finally, Mrs Falcott made an announcement. "Can anyone offer to take a friend and go and look for Luna?" Instantaneously the whole class shot their hands up, hoping to do something other than symmetry, but me and Charlie were picked to go.

I tried to think where she could have gone, it was so puzzling. My brain was working so fast right now and everything was jumbled up. I needed to calm down.

"Look at the floor!" I exclaimed suddenly.

There was Luna's hairband. Then I could hear her shouting desperately for help. We ran to the end of the corridor; an imposing black door was standing in front of us with an electronic lock with numbers flashing. Inside we could hear Luna shouting.

We attempted to open the door, to no avail. Charlie fruitlessly tried to crack the door code.

I knew with my special power I could crack the code, but I was nervous to reveal it. I knew I needed to help so I stepped forward and instantly the numbers started to light up in my head. I tried one combination, it failed. Then the numbers flashed in my brain into a pattern and sequence, and I quickly entered them, and the door swung open.

"Finally," Luna breathed.

I then saw Mr Kowalski appear from the shadows to put a hand over her mouth.

"What are you doing, sir?" I gasped.

"If you're so interested," hissed Mr Kowalski, "this is my protest to become headmaster, but you have foiled it. My plan was to kidnap Luna and hold her hostage!"

At this point, Mrs Falcott burst in. "It's all over, Mr Kowalski. I knew you were up to something. The police are on their way."

Mrs Falcott turned to me and thanked me, and Charlie told her it was my special autistic powers that saved the day.

And that is the story of my first day at school. It has taken time, but I have learned to love and appreciate what makes me different and I am proud.

Archie Seager (9)

The Secrets Of A Cowardly Crook

1st January 2022

Dear journal,

I am, like, so annoyed! Last night, I was caught by the police 'cause I was stealing 200 from my bank account... Fine, I stole it from the local post office. But still...

Anyway, I am Spike Morris, the most wicked crook in the whole of Candlewick! I own this journal, full of stuff that not you nor anyone else are allowed to read or even snoop in. It's full of my secrets so CLOSE THIS BOOK or else I will hack your bank account and take all your money! (What's your account number?)

Unless of course... you can keep a secret, in which case, cross your heart, hope to die, and read on... You're in for quite a ride!

Surprise surprise, you want to keep reading! I mean, just 'cause I'm cute and have big muscles doesn't mean I'm brave and cool, (I would like that though!) so don't expect too much from me as you read on!

So, as I am sitting here in this smelly, cold and mouldy prison cell, I will reveal my first and biggest secret, which I have been keeping for years.

I am scared of... the cops. They watch me all day while I sit here, my legs in chains and write in my journal. Speaking of the fat, twice-retired maniac of a copper, here he comes. Mr Posy (but most of us criminals call him Mr Nosey) is super nosey, poking his big nose into everyone's business. I can't even go into the toilet without him asking what I'm doing! (See what I mean...!)

"Well, well, well, wot do we 'av 'ere?" he said as he waddled over.

This means there's trouble and to be completely honest, I am more than just scared of the police... I'm terrified, petrified!

"Um... h-hello, s-sir," I said.

"Wot, are you doin'?" said Nosey Posy, as he confiscated my JOURNAL!

Guess I'll see you in a minute then...

2nd January 2022

So now I have got my journal back from that loser, I can share my second biggest secret. It is that I'm really scared of deadly ants! Not any sort of ants... robbery philosopher ants (RPA for short)!

These ants rob, money, food and even iPhone 13s! Anyway, they are junior devils!

Well, to be honest, I'm sort of overcoming that fear a little bit. This cell (my police cell) is swarming with the beasts, and they are not as harmful as I first thought they were!

Before this prison stay, I'd be screaming at the creatures, but since you have heard everything I have been saying, you can see how brave I'm being... can't you!?

3rd January 2022

OMG! I'm mind blown! Would you think a child would scare me? You wouldn't after you hear that I'm almost 18 years old! I'm a teenager that's scared of cute kids! That's my 3rd secret, by the way!

Ya wanna know why? Don't get me wrong, I loved my childhood! It was the best even though I got at least 20,000,000 detentions a week (oh, that was fun!). I was given a chocolate bar every day! But now I'm a boring teenager, (annoyingly) I'm only allowed one a week if Mummy says I've been good (I mean Mum).

4th January 2022
So, my 4th biggest secret is that... well... I... I'm kinda scared of the wind. I know what you're thinking, why would a tall, tattoo lover, that's heck yeah sexy and unbelievably vicious and a tiny bit humiliating, be scared of something so silly? And if you ask my sister, Sam, she will agree. I sneak into her smelly bedroom at midnight 'cause I'm scared of the trees blowing and wind howling! (Cheers, Samantha.)
Anyway, I always climb into her tiny sleeping bag, on her huge, 2 sleeper bunk bed, and most of the time... I kind of pee in it... Yeah... I still do that at 17... Moving on!

5th January 2022
So, my 5th secret, and one that you never EVER repeat, is that I really, really love being a princess! Yep! A pink, sparkly, male queen of the night. But of course, the outfits aren't mine, they're my little sisters, but I'm not allowed in her bedroom (unless it's a stormy night) so I have to tiptoe into her dressing room around midnight to make sure she doesn't see me! (#12o'clock #awake #sistersasleep)
But the funniest, most hilarious evening was when I snuck into Silver Street High School for the rich female teenagers' school prom. It was 2019 and I wore a sugar plum fairy dress and a pineapple blonde wig that nicely covered my bald head (I wasn't talking about my extra bold personality, but still!) and funnily enough, I was mistaken for precious Prissy, the daughter of the most famous family in the whole city; the City of Candlewick! The best city in the whole of Old York (New York, but old #worstcountryever, but best city ever!).

6th January 2022

So, particularly weirdly, I have another secret that's just popped into my mind now while I have been writing, so here goes nothing...!

I might have a crush on perfect Prissy...

I think Prissy is more perfect than perfect... Once upon a time, I might have asked the sweet treat out, but who cares!? I know what you're thinking; why would she want to date me? And yes, her and her friends are a pretty mean bunch, but if I EVER come back to my journal writing boo hoo hoo, you're fine to laugh at me! (I would blame her for this of course and would fall immediately out of love with her by the way!)

If you are still reading this far into my journal then thank you, I am truly grateful (mostly 'cause I would only have read less than like 13 words into yours!). But even though I'm taking a break, remember that everything you have read MUST remain a secret for the rest of your goodie two shoes of a life.

Esmay Gillespie (9)

The Abandoned Goldmine

Once there was a group of children and they were all daredevils. They would do anything dangerous or scary together. There were four boys and one girl in the group and their names were Lucas, Sam, Kyle, Nicholas and Jessie. They did anything from riding their bikes in the middle of the road to riding on motorcycles in a skateboard park. If you dare, please read on...

It was the last day of school before the summer holidays and the group was talking in class about what they would be doing for another daredevil mission. Nicholas, the leader of the gang, said to the others that they would be going to the abandoned goldmine to dig up gold tomorrow to see if the rumour about the vampires along with the vampire queen was actually true.

Dring went the school bell which meant it was the summer holidays. All of the students rushed to get outside, including the group. They chatted while going to their homes about the plan for tomorrow but first they got dressed for a party at Jay's house (the richest kid in school). He was throwing a party at one of his mansions and everyone in the year group was invited.

Throughout the party, Jay made a ten thousand pounds hide-and-seek tag competition which ended up with Elisa Jhones (the smartest child in the year group) winning. After the party ended everyone was sad. But the group were excited to do what was going to happen tomorrow.

It was Saturday and the gang was preparing to go to the abandoned goldmine. They packed water and food and flashlights and much more.

When they got there they hopped in a cart that was at the entrance to the mine. Nicholas pulled a lever that was on the side of the cart and they went into the mine...

Jessie switched on the flashlight while the others looked in the distance. Something screeched. "What was that?" asked Lucas.

"Just a bat," answered Nicholas. "There are tons in here."

They went further. At last, the cart went to a halt and they hopped off. "Well, we're walking from here," said Nicholas.

"Yep," agreed Jessie. Another screech.

"I have the feeling that we're being followed by someone," said Sam. "Hmm, strange that there's no gold."

"Yes," agreed Kyle.

They kept on going further, the torch guiding them. They came to a halt because there were two paths to go. "Right, me and Jessie will go to the left and you three boys will go to the right. Oh and before you go, here's a torch and three bottles of water," Nicholas said while handing them out.

They went their separate ways. The three boys walked and walked until they stopped because right in front of them was a dead end. They turned around to see in the light from the torch was a vampire...

Jessie and Nicholas heard the boys scream and they turned around and dashed to them. The moment they got there they found the boys lying unconscious on the ground.

"Oh no, oh no, oh no, what happened here?" asked Jessie sadly.

"Looks like we need to set a camp, it's 8pm," said Nicholas while looking at his watch.

"You brought tents?" asked Jessie.

"Urgh yeah, you know just in case."

"How many?"

"Two, one that holds three and one that holds two. I sleep with Sam and Lucas while you sleep with Kyle."

They slept a long night, well some of them did...

It was the middle of the night and vampires lurked in the mine. One vampire went to a part where they were sleeping and he realised that somebody was in their territory. Vampires do not like when people are in their territory so this vampire did what any unordinary vampire would do... kidnap them...

Jessie woke up to see Kyle awake. "Wow, Kyle, you're alright," said Jessie, pleased. Jessie went to check on her friends in the other tent but she saw that nobody was there. "Okay, we have to go ASAP," she said as they walked and walked and walked.

An hour later and they saw a glimpse of light. Soon they saw shining gold everywhere but they did not only see that but an entire city of vampires. Right in the middle of the small city were the three boys in a cage hanging from the top of the cave.

They waited a little bit for the vampires to go to their houses and then they helped them escape from there. The boys were pleased to see them. Jessie asked them, "Where is the key?"

"It's on the top of the cage," Lucas replied.

She got the key and put it in the padlock to unlock them. Then they ran towards the cart which took them fifteen minutes and then they were off.

Finally, they came back to the exit and Nicholas said, "What an adventure that was."

"Our scariest one yet," agreed Kyle. And they went straight back to their homes.

Back in the mine...

The next morning in the mine the vampires were angry but one vampire was angry enough. "I WILL GET YOU SOMEDAY HUMANS, SOMEDAY!" shouted the vampire queen.

Over the summer they did more scary things and it was back to school soon and they met on the way to their school to chat. "What a summer that was," said Lucas.

"Sad it's back to school," said Kyle with a sigh.

"Yeah," agreed the others.

On the weekends they did more stunts and things got back to normal like they were last time.

Sebastian Kielar (9)

The Diary Of Eliza Wilkinson: The Unusual Last Day Of The Summer Holiday

Dear Diary,
This morning, I woke up at 6.30am thinking everything would be normal... But no. Today is the last day of the summer holidays and I have to do like a million household chores! I mean, who does household chores on the last day of the summer holidays? Don't get me wrong, I love helping Mum, but right now is not the right time.

Last night, Mum gave me strict rules that at 7.50am, my chores start. Argh! I wish I could go on some sort of adventure, like all those characters in books I read. Or I could finish off my latest invention, the Hgih Ylf (backwards for High Fly, an invention where there are jetpacks that have water, food and make you fly!) No one would have guessed that Hgih Ylf is High Fly backwards! And when the money starts rolling in, I'll decide whether I tell them or not. What? I've been talking to you for 80 minutes! Just as I thought, Mum calling, talk soon!

9.00:
Okay, I have just done an hour of chores. Mum gave me 50p. Now I have to clean my mum's room. Then she will give me another 50p. Can't you tell I'm angry? I don't want to keep using that many full stops! Deep breath in, deep breath out. I'm sorry, it's just my mum has like an infinite amount of clothes! Better get to her room. Up the stairs then, shall we?

54

Up in Mum's room:
I'm now in Mum's room starting to clea- Wow! What's this? Mum never showed this beautiful pendant to me! I guess I shouldn't touch it. Oh, Mum won't mind if I just try it on, will she? Ahh, it's sooo beautiful. It looks like the wishing pendant from... from... I don't remember! Okay. Decision made. I'm gonna try it on. Cool, I look really nice in this lovely pend- Arghhh!

In the middle of nowhere:
Where am I? What have I done?! I think I'm in the middle of nowhere! Mum? Mum? Where am I? Where are you? Better calm down. Okay, I'll describe where I am: It's creepy, with trees that have witch-like fingers.
It is sunset now and I can half work out that the wet grass is emerald green. It feels magical here. Okay, I'm going to explore this place. Wish me luck!

Exploring the place:
I ran into the heart of Sunset Forest (I called it that because the sky wasn't changing yet) hoping for the best and wishing I could go home. I didn't say it out loud because I wished to go on an adventure in the first place! At the beginning of my diary, I said this, "I wish I could go on some sort of an adventure, like all those characters in books I read." So maybe this was a wishing pendant and it heard my wish! Well, as I asked for this adventure, I could continue and get home before Mum realised I was gone!
So, let's explore! I tiptoed past a bear in its slumber, ran through a deep mud puddle (luckily, I was wearing boots!), crawled through a hollow log, swayed on the willow tree's leaves and clambered up a tall tree.

I climbed down the tree when I noticed a super-duper deep puddle of water. I stopped in my tracks and put my foot in the puddle. It was so deep! I realised if I went into the water, it would reach my tummy, so I held the pendant and wished for a swimming costume. Time to put the pendant to the test, I guess! And guess what? I was in a swimming costume in no time!

I swam through the long puddle and found a portal at the end! I jumped into the portal, shut my eyes and felt dizzy. I opened them again and saw a world of colour. I decided to keep my eyes closed because I was feeling sick! Finally, I reached my destination (I think!). I walked out of the portal and ran a lot! Then, something on the forest floor caught my eye. I ran over to take a closer look and realised it was a trapdoor. I pulled on the knob as hard as I could, but it just wouldn't budge! Maybe I hadn't seen something stopping the door from opening. After all, it was getting dark. So I held my pendant once again and wished for a flashlight. I turned the flashlight on and searched the door. Bingo! I found a padlock and a note that read:

'Dear Finder,
You have come across Sunset Forest (Ha! I knew it was called that! Anyways, carry on) where all danger lies. You have passed test one like no one else and I'm glad you made it to test two. This trapdoor leads to your home, so if you find the second clue and solve the third, you will go to the fourth. Solve the fourth clue and you will find the key to this padlock. Good luck!

Yours sincerely,
Tom McLane (owner, Sunset forest).'

Okay, let's do this!

The key:
The first clue was next to Tom's note and simply said: 'The tree'. I was confused but then found a piece of paper on the tree opposite me and that was the second clue which said: 'I love purple!' What? There was a purple leaf right next to the tree! This was so easy! The third clue read: 'Bmilc'. This one was hard. A-ha! It was backwards for climb! OMG. Soooo easy! A tree! Again. Fourth clue: 'Log'. On a log? Where is the log? After a bit of running, I found one! Okay, the key is on the tree where I found my first clue! Got it!
Thanks for making the hunt so easy, Tom! I pulled open the trapdoor. Arghhh! I'm back at home! What an adventure. I better go to bed! Wish me luck for tomorrow!
Eliza Wilkinson, 9yrs.

Anhad Kaur Alg (9)

Against The Waves

Fred gazed into the distance in awe. The beach was perfect. It was covered in silky, snow-white sand. Two vibrant, green palm trees danced in the cool breeze and rocks glittered in the scorching sun. It was simply paradise. But what his eyes were staring at was not the sand, nor the rocks, but the sea. The crashing waves greedily swallowed the shore up, spewing out white foam and water and then swallowed it up again.

Clutching the surfboard tightly to himself, Fred raced through the sand and then halfway through, dropped it and ran towards it, his heart pumping loudly in his chest. Next, like a flash of lightning, he slid across the sand and into the waves, the surfboard right under him.

Surfing is extremely thrilling, you feel like you are the king of the sea, with the wind whistling in your ears and the waves rocking you sideways. But surfing sometimes does have fatalities.

Fred suddenly noticed that the lifeguard's flag was red. He then felt slightly scared and lay flat on the board trying to row back to the shore using his hands. But the waves were too rough and too mighty for him. He heard people shrieking at him which made him feel guilty. He had been so careless and stupid.

The tropical beach became smaller and smaller, and the waves rocked him madly. "Help!" he yelped, sounding ridiculously small and quiet, and suddenly, a colossal wave engulfed him whole.

Another slow hour passed by. Fred woke up screaming. He looked around him in fear. Nothing. Just the sea. The waves were calmer now, only swaying him gently back and forth.

He did not know how deep it was, and he did not wish to know. He just floated on his surfboard, hoping that soon he would find land.

The seagulls teased him and pooped on him, and the sky stayed clear-blue, while the sun shone brightly. But it soon began to grow dark, and dusk crept over him. The water gradually became colder and colder and Fred's teeth began to chatter. He wondered whether he would survive the sea when hunger suddenly reached him. He kept thinking about the delicious, mouth-watering pancakes his mum used to make for him. His mouth craved food and his teeth chattered on.

A few hours later, a little dot of sunrise could be seen on the horizon. Then the sky became a river of red, gold and violet as he was welcomed by dawn. The water was now so tranquil that Fred had to paddle with his arms and legs because the current would push him no longer. A little speck of land could be seen in the distance. But then Fred was filled with doubt, would he make it?

It was still extremely far away, and even if he did make it, would he die from hunger and thirst? Fred knew he could not drink the seawater because it would make him sick, and where would he get food? Suddenly, the seagulls caught his eye. But how could he hunt them down? He scanned the sea, but nothing was floating along, not even a small stick. He soon gave up.

The seagulls still cawed at him as if they were laughing at him. Then a huge piece of dark, green seaweed started to float towards him. At last! He picked it up and looked at the birds, grinning. He did not really know what to do with it, so he spontaneously flung the gooey plant at them like a lasso and funnily enough, it caught one of them.

It seemed to strangle the seagull. It flapped its wings in a peculiar way and then plummeted to the sea with a plop! Fred rapidly approached it and picked it up. Then he ripped it into chunks and then looked at the meat in his hand with uncertainty. He stuffed it in his mouth widely and chewed it slowly. It tasted like raw fish and in fact, Fred found it quite appetizing.

But his dry, blistered throat ached for a drink. He had heard that if a person had nothing to drink, they could drink their own urine, but Fred did not want to even think about it. Instead, he swiftly picked the bird up and drained all the blood from it. Fred looked like a tiger finishing off his prey with all the blood around his lips.

He washed his face using seawater when the rest of the gulls unexpectedly started pecking him! Luckily, Fred had a strong reflex, so he immediately lashed out and managed to grab one of their legs and smashed the bird into the water. The others squawked and flapped away in fright. The last one rose from the water, gave the boy a huge peck and afterwards took off, soon disappearing.

Exhaustion hit Fred at once, as he slumped onto his board heavily and breathed in the salty air. He wanted to sleep but firmly told himself not to and tried to paddle in the direction of the speck of land, an island, but he couldn't. He slowly closed his eyes and let out a snore. He was fast asleep. Little did he know that the current was pushing him towards the mysterious island.

Fred suddenly woke up and realised he was in warm waters. He shivered with delight and noticed that the piece of land was certainly closer. He paddled towards it, bursting with hope.

Another day passed, and he never gave up. In the night, he would rest and restore all his energy for tomorrow.
Meanwhile, the island grew bigger, and the water, warmer; soon it felt like a jacuzzi! The island drew Fred closer and closer to it, as if he were under its spell.
Every day he was nearer and nearer until at last, he reached the hot, pink sand - land! He cried with joy and then passed out...

Nina Zych-Twaddell (10)

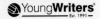

The Secret Paradise

It smelt wet, muddy, and intoxicating. I could hardly
breathe. A stitch pinched my side. I looked down - my new
dress was spoilt. My head was throbbing, and my heart was
pounding uncontrollably in my ears. Was this the end? My
legs could not carry me any further and whatever was out
there would catch up to me in the end. I had a 'B' in running
- mainly because I could not run fast.
Smoke climbed up my nose, just like the chimney sweepers
did back then - though my nose was not a chimney. I
coughed violently and fell to the floor.
I awoke startled. What happened? Was I back in London?
Everything came back to me and crushed my spirits like a
hammer hitting the table. I looked back to the path where I
had come from, but I couldn't tell. All was pitch-black, and
even if there was any hint of light, the overtaking canopy
would take it all away - except for little gaps here and there.
Something rustled in the bushes. With panic in my mind, I
looked around for the source. Maybe and most likely
trouble. I got up and started to run in any random direction
because I knew that if you ran away from the source of
danger, you would stay alive. So that's what I did. A stitch
hit me like a needle being pierced into my skin, but I carried
on - I was looking for somewhere safe to stay for the night,
as a yawn overtook me.
When I awoke the next morning, something wet fell on my
face. It felt like the time when a dog knocked me over and
looked down at me with saliva drooling down its chin.
Possibly this was a dream? But no.

As I got up from the soaked, muddy floor, my eyes started to sting from the falling rain, since I hadn't gotten adjusted to the pouring, acidic water. I hoped the fire from the plane had been put out with rainwater during the night, as it was aggressive.

Putting those thoughts away, I got moving because whatever predators were out there were bound to wake from their slumber and realise easy prey was nearby. I jogged on, as the trees were cloaked in mist, like ghostly, stooped figures with a spidery tangle of leaves. Under me, on the floor of the rainforest, croaked something strange and startling. What could it be?

As I looked below, I realised it was a fluorescent, orange frog! Quite unique, but rather intriguing. Just as I stretched my hand out to pick it up and examine it, a thought hit me - these frogs are poisonous! Oh, how thankful I was to have remembered that!

As I walked on from the venomous creature, I again heard a rustle in the bushes. As adrenaline rushed through my veins, I looked around desperately searching for the source. What could it be? Surely not another frog, it's too petite to make such a significant noise. I decided to carry on - *then I don't have to find out the hard way.* A sigh came to me as I started to jog onward. *There could be a bright side to all of this - when I return to London, I could finally get an 'A' in running.*

Now, all I needed to do was find a secure opening to stay for the night. Whilst doing that, I noticed something quite peculiar on the floor: a little, sea-blue lizard. This time, I thought twice before picking it up, making sure it wasn't poisonous. The puzzling thing was that it didn't try to scuttle away, just as if it wanted to be picked up, like it was waiting for me.

My stomach growled in anguish. All this running had made me very hungry. Starving. I could - but I couldn't, oh what easy prey, but no, I must let it live, and that is final.
"Oh, what a pretty little thing you are! What's your name? Mine is Elizabeth, Elizabeth Mansoori. How about you?"
The interesting creature's tail pointed in a direction, beckoning me to come. I gently put it down and let it lead me, hopefully not to death. I had to run to follow it as it was surprisingly fast for such a small creature. My face hit many branches that were sticking out and added scratches to my already begrimed face.
Suddenly the creature came to a stop, making me trip as I didn't want to crush it by stepping on it.
"Woah... This is awesome! It's so beautiful too!"
I looked down at the lizard, who I noticed was already stepping into this awesome place. I guess it was 'the secure paradise'. I contemplated going in, but then I decided that since the lizard was already gone, so I could too. There were mango trees, banana trees and cherry trees in bloom. A little brook ran in the middle, whilst the grass was greener than I had ever seen. I looked up - the sun was shining unusually bright. Then, I noticed the canopy had been cleared out, but not by force - by nature.
I looked down at the little friend that I had made, who was already helping himself to the mangos! I laughed to myself, as I started to grab a mango too, along with some cherries. I was famished, though I didn't take much, for I could always have more later.

With the seeds of the ripe, delicious fruit, I planted them in the ground by the small, cascading brook. The water was as clear as a crystal, with shoals of fish swimming in harmony. Now and then they would leap in and out of the water, taking turns.

Later, I built a shelter to sleep in for myself and the little lizard and decided to stay there for now at least!

Zara Hussain Turi (11)

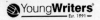
Nature In View

I was going on a trip. I started with the meadow.
I was staring at the deep blue sky. Clouds were drifting
slowly out of sight while the sunbeams were dazzling my
eyes. Faint tears fell to my cheek then disappeared into my
skin. The meadow was full of colour. Green grass swished in
the wind. The grass made my feet tickle while I stepped on it
and the flowers were beautiful. Lovely midnight black roses
and fire red poppies, pink petunias, sunset orange and
yellow tulips, green leaves of a raspberry bush, sky-coloured
bluebells, and purple lavender were spread every which way
I looked. It was an astonishing sight for my dazzled eyes.
An oak tree spread its leaves and dropped nuts. A squirrel
leapt from tree to tree. A bunny hopped along the grass and
a spiky hedgehog slept in his leaf nest. A bird chirped a
lovely little tune from her nest and her babies sang along.
The river flowed downstream and tadpoles swam around in
it. I heard the gentle snore of a tawny owl.

Now to the beach.
On the beach it was lovely. I felt the sand in my toes tickling
me. It was so calm and peaceful. Salty seawater washed
over my face as I dived into the water. Further away I found
a coral reef. There were little fish, big fish, octopuses and
way more but the best thing on the reef was the coral!
There was coral in every colour. Red, orange, yellow, green,
blue, indigo, violet and pink coral. The beach and the reef
were both amazing.

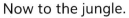

Now to the jungle.
In the jungle it was lovely! Trees stretched to the skies while monkeys were swinging from tree to tree on vines.
A mummy tiger kept watch on her cubs from a nearby tree. The cubs were fighting by the entrance of a cavern. I saw a flower which was a carnivore eating a beetle. A deer was grazing close to the flower. I touched its brown silky fur. It was so soft. It felt like clouds only I didn't know what clouds felt like.
I stared up to the sky, a beautiful robin's egg blue. A great big harpy eagle flew by.

Now back home.
Back at home, I was staring at my books. My books are my treasure and heart. Books are my nature. I love fiction, non-fiction, stories, fables, poetry books, biography books and dictionaries. I treasure really old books and always read my new books.
Reading books brings me to different worlds. My imagination grows huge and gets more spectacular till I burst out whatever story I've got in my head! I either type it or write it, draw pictures of it or read straight away from my head to other people to make their imagination grow as well. Stories and other types of books are amazing and I thank all the authors for these books.

In my garden.
In my garden, a bee buzzed to a flower to pollinate it. A fox leaped onto one side of the fence to the other while a cat stared at it from our neighbour's yard. Our tree stood still and proud and on the top a parrot fed its chicks.

I put my mud bombs with flowers in the middle on a beautiful human statue's hand. I carved the statue out of mud when it was wet. Just then faint raindrops started drizzling down. Some landed on my cheek then disappeared. The raindrops started soaking me so I went inside.

Cosy inside.
I was sitting inside watching my favourite programme. I was sitting next to the fire under a cushy blanket. Also, I was sitting on the sofa with the huge screen in front of me.
My mum was in the garden and Dad at work so I had peace and quiet to watch my programme. I looked beside me, my painting hung on the wall with the photographs Dad took on a vacation to Rhodes in Greece. It was beautiful there. I spent every day on the beach there.

By the lake.
By the lake it was lovely! Fish of myriad colours swam in the freshwater lake. I stared at the fish swimming in the sapphire water. Behind one of the fish was a raging waterfall gushing down the slope. Beside it were coconut trees. I tasted coconut milk. It was a lovely flavour! It was a bit sour and had a milky taste.
I swam in the lake. The water was mild but it felt relaxing to cool off on a hot day. Water trickled down from the steady stream after the waterfall. I could not believe my astonished eyes.

Out at midnight!
I stared up at the sky. The radiant moonlight beamed into my eyes. The night had a beautiful black shade. The stars looked like tiny glowing dots floating in the night sky. A group of stars I spied was shaped like a dog floating and glimmering in space. It was graceful and magical.

A party!

Because we had a few days left of our summer holidays we decided to throw a picnic! We put up decorations and set chairs and food.

We invited my friends Sare and Jannat from school and loads of other friends. We played at the nearby park. We did a relay race, played basketball and football, played at the adventure park, swam in the river and had a paddling race. My dad and I won the race!

We also ate ice cream. My flavour was vanilla, rose and candyfloss ice cream. It was so delicious! After that, we each told stories. I made mine out of the adventures I had in the summer holidays. At last, we built a camp and went to bed. I had lovely dreams.

So long, summer journal, but who knows what else I'll adventure and seek in the last few days of the summer holidays.

Bye-bye summer journal

Love Daphne

Daphne Erkut (8)

The Portal Of Reality

Hi, my name is Daze. I am 13 years old and welcome to the town of Silverhill, where everything has a silver lining! That line went better in my head. Anyway, nothing much happens around here except that I am moving into year 9 next year, and with that, I will be moving into a new school. Honestly, I am going to miss my old school, my friends and Silverhill in general. I have around a week left, so I'd better spend most of it having fun.

I was at my friend Jacob's house, playing the latest Smash Bros game, as we both admired Nintendo. But in this case, Jacob had a tactical advantage, as I preferred The Legend of Zelda, Super Mario, and we both like Pokémon. He obviously beat me.

"Dang it! I almost won that one!" I frustratingly exclaimed. "You must admit I have improved."

"Meh, sort of." Jacob teasingly shrugged.

It was getting late, so I decided to head home. While I was walking down the street, I heard something crash in the distance. It sounded like a tree. I ran in the direction of the sound to check if someone was hurt. Turns out it wasn't a person who needed help, but a dog instead. A tree had fallen on it and the dog couldn't get out.

I tried to lift the tree up, but that was no use. Then I had an idea. I ran back to my house and then went to the garage to get a plank of wood. Once I had come back to the fallen tree with a plank of wood in my arms, I pushed it underneath the tree and then I stood on the other end of the plank. Now the tree was propped up and the dog started to run back home.

"A thank you would have been nice! A bark even, geez!" I shouted. That was quite strange, not many people around here have pets, unless it was a stray dog, but I dusted myself off and started to walk home again.

Once I got home, I immediately fell asleep. This was the last ever normal day of my life as from here on, things are going to get a little weird.

The next day I woke up to sore legs and arms; saving that puppy was more work than I thought. I went downstairs and made myself some breakfast. Today it was an omelette. I gobbled it up and went outside my front porch to breathe in some fresh air. That's when I saw the puppy from yesterday come up to me.

"Hey, little guy! I hope you're better now!" I said sweetly.

"Yes, I am okay now, thanks for asking," said the dog.

Wait a minute... 'said the dog'! I froze in shock. After a while of me just standing there, I eased my muscles and just asked the dog what in the world was going on!

He looked me in the eye and started to walk away, it was as if he wanted me to follow him. I went to catch up with him. He led me deep into the forest where he stopped at what looked like the ruins of an ancient relic.

"This is a relic long forgotten through time. It serves as a portal which can bend reality. It allows people to travel through different timelines, dimensions and universes. It was made by the people of the 1st dimension. I was on a mission to search for other worlds as my dimension is run by animals. Yet the portal broke as I went through. Please help me get back to my world," the dog said.

Huh, what, who, when and why were the only thoughts going through my head. I went blank. Even if this dog needed help, why did it have to happen now? I just wanted to spend the last days of school with my friends.

"Yeah, that's going to be a hard pass. I don't know why you got me into this, I just want to be with my friends. I am leaving," I said harshly.

But then he did it, the puppy eyes. I couldn't resist, so I decided to help him out.

The first shard he said we had to dig up the ground around the area, as he could sense it. So, I picked up a sharp stone and we both started to dig. I think we were digging for over an hour, but at last, my stone hit something. It was the portal fragment! Wow, that was easier than I thought. Only two more remained.

The dog also mentioned that the other portal fragments were not too far from here. The next portal fragment he sensed was in my house. Wait, what? Anyway, we rushed to my house. Turns out my dad found it on the street and decided to take it home.

We snuck past him while he was watching TV. I quickly grabbed the portal piece off his workbench and ran through the door. When I opened my hands, I didn't see a portal piece, I saw a wrench. So, I went back, making sure I took the piece.

One piece left. The last one wasn't as easy to get. It was on top of a tree, a very, very tall tree. The problem was, I am afraid of heights, so I went to get a ladder from my house. I put it up against the tree and climbed all the way up the ladder and tried not to look down. I grabbed the piece out of the tree leaves and slid back down. I felt petrified.

Anyway, I helped the dog finish the portal and it was time to say goodbye. The space gate reignited, and the dog then barked and walked through.

Suddenly, the portal collapsed and turned into ashes. I walked back home and got on my bed and said, "That was tiring, but the holiday was well spent."

Yuvan Nadarajah (11)

My Life Of Wonder

Ordinary

Ordinary! The word that has never been used to describe me. I'm not your typical 11-year-old girl. Yeah, I do ordinary things like reading (well, maybe that's a bit nerdy), drawing and singing but that's who I am. I guess I am normal, inside. But normal kids don't get stared at everywhere they go or make other kids run away.

Oh sorry, I didn't introduce myself. My name's Tia. A plain name, but I think it suits me, besides I don't want a name that attracts attention as I already have enough, although not in a good way. I'm not one of those kids who everyone has heard of because they're a really good singer, actor or really kind. Almost everyone has heard of me, but for a different reason.

So, I bet you've guessed, there's something different about me: however, I won't tell you what... Maybe later when you've really got to know me.

If I found a magic lamp and could have one wish, it would be to look ordinary. To look like everyone else and be treated like everyone else.

My mum had been home-schooling me because she was scared of what other kids might think, say or do and I really didn't want to go to school and I still don't want to. Sadly, she had to go back to work to earn more money for us which meant, I had to go to a 'regular school' - the words I never thought I'd hear.

Films and School

Something that really helps me to forget my troubles is watching films. I can get lost in different worlds and pretend that I'm really cool characters who look normal and nothing like me.

I remember once when I was 6, we had just come back from the park and I had a terrible time. As soon as we got inside, I ran up to my room and turned on the TV to watch my favourite cartoon but just as I started watching it, the screen went black. The power was out! I was devastated and I began to cry. However, Mum telling me I was going to school made me feel worse.

I tried not to think about going to school much but there was always a strange feeling in the air. The night before my personal 'horror film' of going to school started, I couldn't sleep. I kept tossing and turning throughout the night.

The Nightmare

I was walking to school by myself. My head was down while walking as slow as a tortoise. Thick, grey clouds glared, bellowed and followed me the whole time until I saw it: Breecher Prep Middle School. When I reached the gate, the wind blew it shut. Once I finally got it open, I walked timidly through the empty playground. I was late, wasn't I? *What will they think of me?* I thought to myself.

I opened the door to room 231 to find all of the children sitting in their seats in the middle of a maths lesson. The teacher offered me a weird-looking seat in the back corner. I carefully sat down and as I did the seat collapsed! I fell back and felt very embarrassed. Everyone laughed.

I woke up sweaty and panting. I'd had a nightmare.

Going to School

The day had come. I was going to school accompanied by my mum and sister Zoe. As we walked down the road towards Breecher Prep, Zoe was telling me about her first day of school. She said it wasn't that bad. Well, she doesn't look like me!

In the playground, Mum kissed me all over and Zoe gave me a tight hug as they left.

As I approached room 231, a kid in the front row, who I later found out was called Archie, asked, "Err... who are you and what's wrong with your face? I think you're lost 'cause this ain't an inclusion school."

That's when the laughter started - hysterical laughter.

"That's enough. Settle down. This is Tia and she'll be joining our school," Miss Harper, my teacher, shouted.

Introduction morning went by fine. There were a few looks but that's normal. However, I wasn't looking forward to lunch as the thought of all the many children in one place scared me.

I found a small table in the corner and started eating my much-loved tuna sandwich.

"So you never answered my question before. Were you in a fire or something?" the same kid from before questioned.

Chloe - Fortune Favours the Bold

I know how hard starting a new school can be. I started Breecher Prep last year. Archie used to pick on me because of my accent. I used to live in England, but my parents split up, so now I live with my mum in a small flat as she got a job here in America.

'Fortune favours the bold', Mum would always say. So last year, I learnt to stand up to bullies and I'll help others do it too because it can be hard at first.

It Might Not Be So Bad After All

"Archie, leave her alone," bellowed a girl with long, brown hair. "Stop being so horrible." She stared right at him with a threatening look on her face.

Archie backed off. She turned to look at me, suddenly looking much nicer, and said, "Take no notice of him. Oh, by the way, my name's Chloe. Chloe Williams. What's yours?"

"Tia," I answered, "Tia Anders." We talked for the rest of lunch, and at that moment, I knew it might not be so bad after all.

Isabelle Asiedu (11)

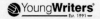

The Mysterious Island

There once were three characters called June, Kevin and George who were famous explorers from around the world. These three famous explorers were about to travel the world in 40 days, all from separate destinations and they didn't have a clue about each other and about the adventure they were about to embark on.

Now it's time for you to meet the explorers... June was an explorer who had travelled far and wide but this was going to be her biggest adventure. June had short brown hair with light blue eyes. Her equipment was a bag with three bottles of water, food, a camera and a positive attitude. She made sure to take memorable photos of every destination that she visited.

Kevin was a world-famous explorer. He specialised in deep water exploration and had travelled to deep dark jungles. Kevin had long black hair with orange and green eyes and looked like a rock star. Kevin was a demolition expert who loved to blow things up. All he had in his bag was explosives, food and water. Kevin couldn't wait to set off on his adventure and explore the new island.

George was new to exploring but had a keen eye when it came to antiques and items of value. George had blonde wavy hair and green eyes. George loved science and had a bag full of science equipment, food and water.

These explorers were at the same airport in Egypt and were travelling to the same destination which was a mysterious island. When at the airport, they had to show their passports, they were all of a similar age. June and Kevin were in their 30s and George was 41 and it was his birthday. When they were ready, they hopped on the plane and started their amazing journey to the mysterious island.

They reached their destination and this is when they met. June said, "Do you want to explore the island together?" Everyone replied with excitement, "Yes! Let's do it!" They set off walking deeper and deeper into the jungle. Suddenly, they stumbled across a bright light coming from a cave. They all decided to check what was going on. When they got closer to the cave, something very strange was going on inside. They could see what looked like a cartoon dimension and what seemed like a huge monster. The smaller minions were calling the monster Game Bot. There were two minions, known as Bloop and Bleep, which travelled behind the monster. They looked like walking remotes. The monster, known as Game Bot, actually looked like a huge console.

The three adventurers observed what was going on in the cave. They could see that the game bot and his minions came through the cartoon dimension and were clearly trying to escape something that was also possibly coming through the dimension!

Game Bot shouted, "Quick! Let's run and hide from the enemies."

TP Mummy and Melviafin and many, many more were on their way through the dimension. The three of them ran towards the cave to see what was going on and when they crossed the dimension they realised they had turned into cartoon characters!

"Did you just see that?" shouted June. "Turn back around and go back. I don't want to be a cartoon character and look like this!"

On the dimension, there were four emeralds all placed on each side and top and bottom.

George shouted, "Quick Kevin, try and remove one of the emeralds."

Kevin reached out and grabbed the closest one on the side. The three of them ran and hid in the bushes facing the dimension. They could see lots of enemies running like they were heading out of the dimension but when they crossed over, something strange happened. They would either turn into food or people, some even turned into animals or even objects like rocks.

"It must have been when Kevin removed the emerald," shouted June.

TP Mummy approached the exit of the dimension and when she crossed over she still looked the same, like a woman covered in bandages with yellow beady eyes and super fearsome. She saw them and gave chase! The three of them ran away until they suddenly stumbled upon a huge slug.

June shouted, "Watch out!"

When TP Mummy came, she got swallowed by the slug's long slimy tongue and that was the end of her. Suddenly, when they were running, they fell through a hole in the ground which took them to a tomb.

Kevin quickly said, "Can I do something?"

The others said, "Yeah! Do it!"

All they heard was a big boom. Hidden amongst the rubble were gems and gold like you had never seen before!

George said, "Wow! We are rich, so so rich!"

At the bottom of the tomb, they could see another dimension and when they got closer, they could see dinosaurs, so many dinosaurs. They all thought, *not again!* They scampered away with gems and gold in every pocket they had.

80

June, Kevin and George escaped the mysterious island with lots of treasure which had never been seen before and because they were explorers they decided to give it to the British Museum. To this day, you can go and see this amazing find on display.

Alexander Hunt (9)

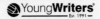

Copycat Crew

In an almost perfect house lived a blue-eyed, brown-haired girl called Lily. She had a brain that was like a puddle of wisdom, full of curiosity and courage. Lily's heart was an angel's nest full of music notes of joy, happiness and hope. Lily had two older siblings called Daniela and Isabella, their mother and father loved them dearly. Between the three sisters, they had one pet called Rose, who was 9 months old and was a snowy white, active kitten.

On a beautiful, breezy summer day, Daniela and Isabella decided that they wanted a cat of their own, so they did not need to share with Lily. As soon as the sun came out, they drove off to the pet shop.

When they got to the door they strolled in and stood in the middle of the huge hall staring endlessly at all of the excited, overwhelmed pets waiting to be adopted. After a few hours, Daniela and Isabella finally chose a white, active kitten that was identical to Rose. The two sisters could not wait to adopt their chosen kitten, they found out the kitten was called Rosie.

When they arrived home the two cats stood and stared at each other for quite a while but when they finished staring at each other they joyfully took a wander around the house to explore. They played and then played some more until the sun began to fade away and it was time for dinner. After they had dinner, they both felt exhausted, so they fell asleep as soon as the clock struck nine. They dreamt about what exciting things they could do tomorrow.

When they both woke up, they found Daniela, Isabella and Lily were already awake. At that very moment, Rose and Rosie heard Daniella and Isabella say to Lily that they no longer wanted a pet kitten as the two kittens were always together rather than playing with the sisters, so Lily now had two kittens all to herself, just as she always wanted. Instantly Lily picked up both kittens and took them to her room so she could have a little bit of alone time with Rose and Rosie, without her two ever-so-annoying sisters.

After what felt like two hours, but was only half an hour, Lily started to fall asleep. When Lily was fast asleep a minute passed then ten minutes passed and after a long time, Lily finally woke up to two disturbing footsteps that strode through the door. "What have you been doing for the last..." There was a pause... "two and a half hours?" Daniela boomed, half listening to what her sister was just about to say and half being rude, looking at her brand-new iPhone. Lily did not bother to say anything and just shook her head and did a little smirk.

Lily headed downstairs and saw her two kittens playing joyfully together but something felt a bit strange because the two kittens were doing exactly the same thing at exactly the same time. The two kittens were playing catch with a ball of yarn but instead of throwing it, they rolled it around. They also loved running around in tiny circles, one behind the other.

Lily thought hard for a moment and then thought a bit more until she decided to keep her eye on them at all times for four hours. If they kept being suspicious, she would tell her mother and father about what had been happening and possibly take them to the vet.

After four hours, the kittens were still looking very suspicious, so Lily went to tell her mother and father all about it. When she finished telling them they decided to take Rose and Rosie to the vet.

When they got out of the car, they both gave a confused cat purr. Lily knew that they were wondering why they had come to the vets. Was it because they were poorly? They did not know but they were determined to find out.

Although they had an appointment, it was a long wait. When it was finally their turn to go to the vet, they explained why they had come. Unfortunately, the vet did not know anything about why they had been acting strangely recently. Then the vet said... "The person where you got your pets from will know a lot more than me, so I recommend you go there to find out a bit more information."

Lily said, "Thank you," got back in the car and travelled to the pet shop. When they arrived, they told the person behind the counter about how the two kittens had been acting strangely.

But the shopkeeper just laughed and said, "It's because they are twin sisters! Their mum is owned by someone called Elizabeth Mary Simpson."

"She's my friend from class and I go round to her house every Friday so I can take Rose and Rosie over as well!" Lily interrupted.

When they got in the car Lily was so happy that they knew what was going on with Rose and Rosie and very excited to learn that they were twin sisters. As soon as they got home Lily wanted to make up a crew for just her and the two kittens to be part of. She thought and thought and came up with a perfect name. She did a drum roll and then said...

"Ladies and gentlemen, boys, and girls, I am so happy to call me, Rose and Rosie... The... COPYCAT CREW! We cannot wait to have lots of fun adventures together."

Indiana Nicol (8)

The Lost Dragon

Chapter 1: The Prank

"Hey, wake up! It's the first day of school," shouted Ella.

"Five more minutes," mumbled George.

"Change into your uniform and go down for breakfast."

I wish I was watching TV right now... Poof... George was too lazy to wake up.

"AAAHH!" shouted George.

"Who are you?"

"Hi, I am your friendly genie. I am here to-"

"Oh Dad, don't prank me, you've done this to me many times."

"Excuse me... I am not your dad, and I am tired of making wishes come true, so I will only be willing to give you one wish."

"I am so happy!" screamed George with excitement.

"But remember, George, use it wisely!"

"Firstly, how do you know my name? Secondly, you can trust me," said George. "I wish for a DRAGON!" shouted George.

"George, you just wasted a wish," the genie quietly said.

"What? It was a great wish," said George.

"A great wish? More like a stupid wish. Now go to school."

"Oh! I forgot I have a test. I better get going. Mum!" shouted George.

Nobody replied.

"DAD! ELLA!" he screamed. "I guess I am walking to school."

"One hour late on your first day and you missed your test!" shouted Mrs Smith.

"But I-I-" mumbled George.

"No buts and no excuses. Go to the principal's office..."

"Dang it," muttered George.

"What are you doing in my office?" asked the principal.

"The teacher sent me here," said George.

"Who is your teacher?"

"Mrs Smith."

"It's okay, you are allowed to go back to your class now. Before you go, what is your surname?" asked the principal.

"It is pretty long but I can tell you. Harrysteventadgonemad harryverseslarrystayshrimpslouisegottoit."

"Well that is long," said the principal. "You better go back to your class."

"Hey, miss... can I get in?"

"It's madam, how are you back?"

"The principal told me to go back to class."

"No, you are not. I am sending you home..." The teacher was angry.

"Yesssss!" George cried with joy.

Back at home.

"Ella, where is your brother?" asked Mum.

"I don't know, Mum."

"What?"

"I think he is at school."

"School? During summer holidays?"

"I kind of pranked him..."

Mum's face turned red. "You are grounded. I am going to look for him..."

Mum rang the school.

"Is this Mrs Harrysteventadgone?" asked the teacher.

"No, why?"

"Well... there is a boy named George and he is not supposed to go to my class," said Mrs Smith.

Mum hung up. "I am getting George right now..."

At school... "I am walking home," said George.

George already left school when Mum arrived.

When Mum came back, George was watching the TV.

"Why did you go to school?"

"Because Ella told me to go."

Chapter 2: The Dragon

"OMG! I am so scared of dragons. AAAH!"

The house was very noisy.

"That's my dragon!" screamed George with excitement.

"What? A dragon? A real dragon?" Mum shouted.

"I am going to ride it outside," said George.

George went outside and played with the dragon.

Chapter 3: The Lost Dragon

George had just woken up.

What a beautiful day, I have to play for a full day outside with my dragon, he thought.

"Oh no! My dragon is lost..."

George looked for the dragon everywhere in the house, but he couldn't find it.

"Mum, I can't find my dragon..." cried George.

"Well, I saw him going that way." Mum pointed to the kitchen. Ella was there.

"Ella, have you seen my dragon?"

"Yes, I saw it went into the back garden."

Dad was in the back garden lying on the chair.

"Dad, have you seen my dragon?" cried George.

"No, George, let me take a nap," said Dad.

"Wait, I see the back door open," cried George.

"Oh really?" said a familiar voice.

"Genie? ...Is that you?"

"Yes, George."

"What are you doing here? Where is my dragon?"

"I came to say what a terrible job you had done. You didn't put a leash on the dragon, so he almost escaped. So I am going to take him back."

"But aren't leashes for dogs?"

"No, you fool... they're for almost all animals..."

"Could you please give my dragon back... I promise I will look after him from now on."

"Okay, I will give you one more chance, take him. If you don't obey my instructions, I will take him back."

George agreed. The Genie disappeared.

Ringggg... The school bell woke him up.

"Were you sleeping, George?" asked Mrs Smith.

"Where... where's... my dragon...?"

"A dragon... What are you talking about?"

Everyone in the class laughed. George realised that it was a dream.

Ameya Nair (9)

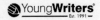

My Journey

Okay, this story starts off with one, two, three characters. Meet my mum and my dad and me. We went to Ireland; it was so fun going on the plane and I finally stepped into a new world.

We got to stay at my dad's cousin's house. We stepped in and I saw a clock that was made from flowers. I was shocked. I wandered upstairs and saw a button; it said 'push me'. Can you guess what I did? I pushed it on. The stairs became a slide. I went down and there was a ball pit. I was so excited. I went down once and I could do this forever, but we did have to go to a water park.

When we got there, we waited so long it took one hour to wait in the queue. When I got in it was like a sauna. I was very scared going down the slides, but I did it and I loved it. Then I looked up and saw a three-foot slide. It was so fast, big, and scary.

At the water park, there were so many things to do; not only was it a water park, but it was an arcade as well with a Ferris wheel, bumper cars, golf and even a mini Go Ape at the end.

After all the fun we had to go home. And can you guess what I did when I got home? The same second we got home, I went on the slide. Later that night, we all went to bed. Then we had to wake up the very next day. Can you guess what time? 3 o'clock in the morning. I was exhausted. We went through security (not my favourite part). After that we got in the airport gift shop. I bought snap cards, a soft toy sheep and a sheep Rubik's cube. I love sheep and pigs and bears; I was so happy.

I finally got home; I missed my house. A few weeks later my cousin Hannah asked me if I would love to go to Kent with her. And can you guess what I said? Yes.

When we arrived, their house was a mansion and they had two cute dogs, Blue and Teddy. We stayed there for five days; I was exhausted every time I woke up. However, that was an amazing, busy time.

Two days later we went to Hollywood Bowl, aka bowling. I got so many points. After the last two days on the last day, we went back to my cousin's house in London. We went home, had dinner and I had not seen my mum and dad for five whole days. I was so happy to see them again.

Me and my sister performed at summer school. I played one of the lead roles, Troy Bolton. After three days of practice dancing, singing, and acting, that was when we could finally perform our piece at the Alexandra Theatre. Every time we went on the stage it was so hot. The lights shined in my eyes. It was an amazing feeling to come back again on a stage.

After our performance, we went to a place called Bonete Lounge. Me and my sister got fries, they were so delicious. After that, we went home and finally my sister left, but I still had my big sister with me.

Then two weeks later, school came. I was excited but nervous at the same time, but now I am in year five, it was a bit scary.

Next week I am going to a concert in London. I am so excited, but sometimes I do not like loud noises, but sometimes I do, depending on how I feel. I am just so excited 'cause I am finally going to see my sister again.

After a few weeks, we finally got a hot tub. It is so cool at night-time because it has LEDs on the bottom of the hot tub and they shine through to the top of the hot tub to create colours like red, blue, pink, green, white, orange, turquoise, and so many more. On the hot tub, they have impressive cool lights, pillows and the bubbles are just so fun to watch and see them expand into huge bubbles.

Yesterday we went to my auntie's house, and it is so nice, and her bed is comfortable. They have two pets, a bunny and a dog called Vixy, and her breed is a German shepherd. She loves playing tug of war and ball catching. She is incredibly good at lying down, jumping, sitting, and shaking her paw.

Me and my mum and my dad went to the beach. They got fish and chips with salt and vinegar. It was so good. I got popcorn chicken.

Me and my mum then went to the lavender fields. It was so nice. Me and my mum did a mini photoshoot. It was a scorcher outside, so we decided to get ice cream. They had limited edition lavender, cotton vanilla, cotton chocolate and raspberry sorbet and after our ice creams, we went to the Lordington lavender shop. Me and my mum could not decide what to get so after an extended period, we finally decided what we wanted to buy. We bought lavender essential oil, lavender cream, lavender candles, and lavender soap bars. In each corner of the fields, all you could smell was lavender. I loved it there only because it made me feel so calm after being there. It was a special day out with my mummy.

After a few hours of journeying, we went home and had a lovely dinner. We had chicken. Once I cut into it all you could see was garlic oozing out, it was scrumptious.

After I had a bath and got into my avocado PJs, I went downstairs and watched TV. Can you survive while watching? I fell asleep on the sofa.

Adele Bagdonas (9)

The Most Magnificent Trip To Scotland

Me and my family planned a trip to Scotland. While I was asleep, my dad carried me to the car. I woke up after three hours and I saw we were in the car. I was so confused as to where we were going.

I asked my mum, "Where are we going?"

My mum said, "Scotland, darling."

I was like oooh. Then I realised we were going to Scotland because this was the day we planned it. On the way there, my mum booked two rooms at a hotel. We got there but in the car park, we had to wait because it opened at nine-thirty.

When it opened, me and my mum went to get the cards for the rooms, but I had to translate to my mum what the woman at the register said because my mum doesn't know that much English, so I helped her. We went back to the car and me, my dad, my mum, my grandmother and my auntie carried the bags to the rooms.

After we got to the rooms, we lay in bed because we were tired. Then we went on the train and went to Edinburgh. We saw a castle, but we couldn't see inside it. Then we went back to the hotel and after an hour, we went back to the castle. It looked awesome. It had different colours. After we did some pictures, we went back to the hotel. When we got to the hotel, we went to our rooms and went to sleep.

The next day, we went back to the castle and we saw some of our friends from Northampton. I played with the boy and took some pictures. We then looked around Edinburgh with them and found a restaurant. We said goodbye and went back to the hotel and we went to sleep.

94

We woke up and we got dressed. We got on the train and went to Edinburgh.

When we got there, we got on a bus, but not a usual bus, it was an unusual bus because it told you about all the places. My mum paid and when we got on it, they gave us glasses and headphones. We went up in the front of the bus. We set off and they told us about Scottish history. They told us about the castle that the queen had and about the gardening centre, about a theatre, about a strange hotel. Then, at the last stop we got dropped off and we climbed rocks. I think it was the best one.

Then a different bus came. This was a usual bus, but I think that was still fun because we could see cool stuff that does matter to me. When we arrived back, we went straight to the train station and went back to the hotel to eat and change clothes.

We went back to the castle to take some more pictures. It just looked so good, that's why we always went there and took pictures. After we finished, we went back to the hotel to go back to sleep.

The next day, we dressed, ate our breakfast and went to Edinburgh. My mum said we should go to the beach. We took the bus and went a few stops, but we didn't stop at the end, we had to walk a bit to get there. From the bus, we saw jokers on the roof of the pub. When we got off the bus, we saw a giraffe and an elephant. We took pictures with them. Then we walked towards the beach. When we got there, we were hungry. We saw a fish and chip shop.

I said, "The fish has plastic in it."

My mum said, "There is no plastic in the fish."
I ate it and I was fine with that because I got ice cream after, my favourite. I finished my ice cream and went in the sand to play while they ate their ice cream. Then we had to go and look around the beach. We had to go back to the bus station by walking there. When the bus came, we got on it and went to the train station to go to the hotel.
When we got there, we changed and went to the castle like usual, to take pictures. After we finished, we went back to the train station. When the train came, we went on it and we went to the hotel. When we got there, we went to sleep and washed because the next day, we had to go on the road.
The next day, we woke up and dressed then went downstairs to eat breakfast. After we finished eating, we went back upstairs. We started to pack. When we finished packing, we took the bags downstairs to the car. Me and my mum had to drop the cards at the reception, but we had to wait because there were people in front of us. We waited, waited and waited till it was our turn. We gave the cards. I had to translate to my mum.
We got in the car and drove. My family talked and talked. While they were talking, I was watching YouTube. Then I started talking too. After that, me, my grandmother and my auntie started to play a game. Then my mum stopped us for no reason. We stopped to get ice cream again. We went to get it from the gas station. We jumped in our car. When we finished eating, we went. We had one hour remaining.

96

Finally, we got home. We ate something and after we ate, we went to sleep. It was relaxing. After this trip I finally found out that Scotland is the perfect place to go and have a nice time with your family.

Delia Maria Sasek (10)

The Four Seasons

The snow glistens as it falls from the sky
The sledges being brought outside
A magical feeling is in the air
Children enjoying the snow
On the days when the wind sings, clumsy children come out
to play with me
On the days when the wind blows, more marching soldiers
fall from the sky
On the days that I am stormy, cold children stay inside
However, there is always time to build magical creatures
with me
Or throw snowball after snowball
Go ice skating on the ponds I mildly cover
Everybody loves playing with me
I am their pet
I bring joy to them
When they wake up in the morning and see me fall from my
home
They rush out to make snow angels with me
The parks are crammed with people trying to touch me
How I bring joy to everyone
Sliding, building and throwing me
When the day is done I fall from the sky once more
When people see me come the winter is there
Young or old, everyone loves me
Slipping, sliding and carefully walking down the streets

Wherever they go they always like playing with me, slippery
Snow
Those who like to tickle my belly while skiing or
snowboarding down the slope
However, when the sun is at its highest at around mid-day
people stop but not for long
Then they come and see me again
When the winter comes to an end people are sad to see me
leave
But remember I am always there in your heart
Slippery Snow.

The sun shines as merry children laugh
Licking their ice cream on a warm sunny day
Everybody laughing thanks to me, shiny Sun
I am a golden star like the main act at a theatre play
Laughing, bathing or playing, everything is a joy
My bright light shines down on people, old or young
Making everybody feel special
A joyful atmosphere filling up everywhere
People tickle my insides or give me a smile
At my strongest point even an irritating smile
I travel around the world, loving everything I see: happy
faces and blistering smiles from ear to ear
I cuddle everybody I see as you are all friends to me
Whether scooting or swimming, dancing or playing
Everybody is warmed by me
Near the school end, I am lots of fun
Sliding down the slide or merely having a stroll

I bring pleasure to everyone
Making cold water cool
I am much loved by one and all
People scramble to get a sight of me
Taking in as much as they can
Even travelling to the other end of the world, just to get a
glimpse of me
But when the sun turns into shade, I wave back at people
sad to see me go
But I remind them I will be back soon
And remember my humble wise words
I am always there in your heart
Shiny Sun.

The wind rustles as the leaves fall below
Children playing in the crisp brown leaves
Laughing and tickling me
They jump up and down in me
Grown-ups laugh to see such fun and join in very soon
I am a wonderful sight
Everybody loves me whether young or old
Playing with me or jumping around
I create a magnificent atmosphere
Beautiful, crisp leaves fall from the trees
People smiling at them to know I have come
The bare trees, one of my many mysteries
All the things to see and do,
While I, Autumn, am there too

They see me as a new start ahead
Or simply as more fun ahead
With Halloween in spooky costumes
Or simply the fun with nature
Autumn has something for you all
Whether plain or creative,
The joy and fun is for everyone
Tickling my back or rolling around in me
A magical spirit filling the air
When the sun turns down below and snow starts to fall
People are sad to see me go
But remember my words
I am always there in your heart
Awesome Autumn.

When the sun starts to glisten to and fro
People know that I, Spring, have come
The new animal generation to be
Is the nickname of me
Happy lambs jump around, accompanied by their ever-
caring mothers
Little fowls steadily learn to run and jump
I love the smiles on everyone's faces
Whether playing or having fun,
People love to see me come
A heart-warming atmosphere is all around, people playing
and laughing
They tickle my belly or tickle my toes

My open-heart glowing on them all
My happiness spreading around
People welcome the time of fun
Whether playing or enjoying things
People wish to see me
Smile at me
Laugh with me
Or even say hello to me
I am much loved by people around
Not too warm nor too cold,
I, Spring, am the perfect weather for you all
In spring there is something for everyone: the Easter Bunny
or merely spending time outside
People play in the park or go outside,
They love me as I am so much fun
Their laughs and smiles printed in our memories for the days
to come
But when the sun gets stronger, I sadly wave goodbye
But remember I am always there in your heart
Sophisticated Spring.

Alexandra Desbiens (12)

Princess Rose's Fairy Adventure

Once there was a castle. A king lived in the castle. The king lived with his daughter. The princess was called Rose. Princess Rose was feeling a little fed up. She lay in her room which was in the tallest turret and dreamt of adventures. *Wackazoo!* A witch appeared.

"I am the good witch from the forest of dreams." She poured Rose a magic cup of tea. "Drink this tea and you'll transport anywhere you dream of."

She took a sip. *Wackazoo!* She ended up in the dark forest. She picked up some sycamore seeds. When she blew them, they fell to the ground and turned into little fairies. The fairies danced with delight. Princess Rose couldn't believe her eyes.

One of the fairies sprinkled fairy dust on Princess Rose and *poof!* Princess Rose was little! One of the fairies waved her wand at Princess Rose and she grew fairy wings.

"The fairy magic will only last for a day," said another one of the fairies.

They took her to the music room which was under a pleated inkcap. They listened to the piano playing a familiar tune, then they played on the flower merry-go-round. After that, they sat down in the light of the full moon.

"I have had the most wonderful time, but I must get back to the castle."

Just then, a shooting star went by. She closed her eyes. *Wackazoo!* She was back home.

Olive Robson (5)

Heart

Halie had always loved the beach. Every morning, she would race down to her sandy haven, all the way from her family's sun-bleached cottage, to search for treasure. She never searched for gold or silver, buried by pirates from long ago, no, she searched for things more special than that, objects which rattle with a thousand stories of where it may have come from, and the things it may have seen.

Her little Jamaican island was a treasure hunter's heaven. Under her bed, she kept the most precious of her treasures. These included several spiralling shells (witch's fingers that were once curled with claws, more like a cat than a person's), a silver locket, which may have hung around an English woman's neck when the Britons first arrived here, and a piece of wood with strange carvings down the side of it - perhaps a relic from the ancient Jamaicans that lived here.

This morning, she was paddling in the surf. She liked coming down here before school when there were no busy tourists to break the island's peaceful silence. It was an exhilarating feeling, standing there, with the wind whipping her hair around her face, a tropical bird screeching somewhere in the palm trees nearby, and her feet, sunk deep in the sand with the waves gushing around her. Halie pulled her feet out of the sand that her ankles were sinking into. She smiled. Just then, she noticed something peculiar in the turquoise water below, a shiny, sapphire-blue stone.

Halie stooped over and picked it up. She brushed her braids from her face as her fingers pierced the salty water. She felt the stone with her wrinkled fingers. It was jagged along the edges like it was a smaller piece cracked off from a bigger one.

With her new-found treasure, she began to make her way home. Wading through the water, churning up the sand, slapping her bare feet on the concrete, she reached the front door and raced upstairs straight away, but her Mum shouted, "Whatever you be doin' up der, sunshine, you better hurry for dat school bus before it leaves!"

Halie paid no attention, as some mad urge had seized her, one that made her unable to draw her attention away from the stone, and raced into her bedroom anyway. She sat down, cross-legged on the bed, and fingered the rock. It shimmered with an unearthly glow, and the more she stared at it, the more she loved it.

But then Halie's heart filled with terror. Little black dots were creeping up her arms, like ink spatters, forming elaborate tattoos that actually moved! Little golden flecks glistened on her fingers, a pair of green turtles swimming up her arms, and little goldfish paddling on her palms and the back of her hand.

On the back of her hand, right in the centre, was a heart. Blue, and shiny, just like her rock. Halie noticed that there was a tiny bit of rock broken off, just like the stone that she was holding at that exact moment!

Suddenly, a noise, a little bit like wind chimes, echoed through Halie's body. And there was a rustling, hissing noise, like whispers being carried on the wind. They said, "We are the heart of the ocean. We are pieces of one, separated hundreds of years ago. Throw us back in where we belong."

Halie promptly dropped the rock onto her soft blanket. The drawings vanished. Halie knew what she had to do. She sprung off her bed and picked up the rock. The tattoos slowly began to seep back onto her skin, slowly but surely, and as she raced down the stairs, her Mum screeched "You silly girl! That bus just left and if you aren't goin' to school right this instance I-" But the rest of her words were cut off, as Halie closed the door. She didn't care. All she wanted was for the rock to return to the sea.

Halfway down to the beach, Halie suddenly began to feel dizzy. Her vision slipped out of focus, and as she looked down, she realised that the illustrations had reached her legs, seaweed wrapping itself around her legs. She stumbled as she reached the sand, and tripped as she approached the water. Had she looked in the mirror at that moment, she would have seen her usual walnut-brown eyes become a deep blue, shells stencilled on her cheeks.

With all her remaining strength, she threw the stone back into the sea. It landed with a plop, and Halie never saw it again. She never told anyone what happened that day, not even when she turned up at school sand-smothered and drenched in salty water. I hope you won't tell anybody either.

Eve McDonald (10)

In The Woods

On a bright and dazzling day, me and my parents went to get some groceries and things from Lidl for my grandmother. We bought cauliflower, broccoli, plates and carrots. My father bought me chocolate.

As we walked home, a freaky, strange man stalked us. I turned around and he pulled me and took me to the spooky, eerie and dark woods. My parents tried pulling me back but it was no use. Hence, they told me that they would look for help. The woods were pitch-black, exactly how it was when my eyes were closed. The man turned the switch on the torch. Thereafter, he tied me up and went to sleep.

I sweated with fear and crossed my fingers that my parents would come and help me fast. Instead of my parents, a thoughtful boy named Andrew came and helped me. Before the man woke up, Andrew untied me and took me to my parents. I was so happy and I thanked him so much. He felt like there was no problem in helping a girl. I thought it was embarrassing. My parents thanked him too.

Subsequently, we reported the bad man to the police. We searched for Andrew's address, took him there and went home.

I woke up and found out that it was just a dream. I laughed at myself, washed my face and went downstairs to eat pancakes with syrup. Even my parents had the exact same dream as me. We all laughed and said, "It was just a dream!"

Kasvini Kaanthan (8)

Ten Minutes

It was New Year's Eve. Me and my family were getting ready for our annual celebration. Every year, everyone gets 10 minutes to time travel to wherever they want in their lives. I already knew that I was going to travel to next New Year's to see how much I had changed. However, you can't travel forward more than one year. You can't actually talk to yourself, but you can view.

Everything was ready. The bright Christmas lights, dancing around the room, the sweet smell of chocolate cake wafting around and the pop of the champagne bottle as we all cheered. Two minutes left to go. A grin spread across my face. "Anna, be careful," sighed my mum. I rolled my eyes at her and watched as the clock began to count down.

"Ten, nine, eight, seven, six, five, four, three, two, one! Happy New Year!" we chanted.

Suddenly, the room vanished. Everything turned pale white as I was lifted up into the air. "Where do you want to go?" bellowed a mysterious voice.

"A year from now," I replied as I shut my eyes.

A gentle click bounced around. All the walls faded, as well as the white light. It was time. I opened my eyes and looked around. "It's all... black!" I said quietly to myself. There was nothing surrounding me except darkness. Darker than I had ever seen before. Confused and worried, I started panicking. Maybe it was nothing? Maybe it was all a dream? I shut my eyes again and waited.

A few minutes later, I woke up again in our living room, the chocolate cake still on the table, the bottle of champagne waiting to be poured and the colourful Christmas lights delicately twinkling. Everyone was now back in the room.

"That... was amazing!" yelled my older brother Joseph. "We have a dog, a new house with a massive TV and my room is perfect! Although, I didn't see you, Anna," explained Joseph.
"Neither did I," said Mum.
"Or me," replied Dad.
"Must've just been a glitch," I replied.
"You need to tell us if it was just black," stated Mum.
"Why?" I asked.
"It's not important, was it black?" she continued.
"No, I saw the dog and the new house," I lied.
"Promise?" she asked.
"Yes, Mum," I replied.
Dad carefully cut the cake into even slices and handed each of us a piece. Joseph engulfed his within a few seconds while I sat there staring at mine. "I'm not hungry," I explained as I ran towards my room. I could tell everyone was confused. I slammed the door and sat on my bed. *Why was it black? Why was Mum worried? Was it just a glitch?* I thought to myself as I drifted off to sleep.
The next morning, I got out of bed and went straight to the bathroom. To my surprise, no one was in there. I brushed my teeth and headed downstairs. Mum was making fried eggs in the kitchen. I sat down at my usual spot at the dining table and waited.
"Good morning!" I yelled from the dining room. There was no reply. Perhaps she didn't hear me. "Good morning!" I yelled again but there still was no reply. I sighed and walked towards the kitchen. "Mum! Can't you hear me? I said good morning!"

Still no reply. I let out an exasperated sigh and reached out towards her shoulder. However, my hand slid through. It was like I was a ghost or something. Panicking, I waved my arms through her but they kept on sliding through.

"Anna! Come have your breakfast!" she yelled upstairs.

"I'm right here, Mum," I replied. Mum didn't answer.

A few moments passed. She let out a deep sigh and marched towards my room.

"Anna! I told you to come downstairs and have your breakfast!" she said as she opened the door.

"Anna? Anna? Where are you?" she continued as she searched around the room. She began to panic.

Suddenly, Mum lifted up the blanket and screamed. Joseph and Dad rushed into the room. Mum had tears streaming down her face. They all peered over to stare at what was under the blanket. Joseph was so shocked, Dad was even more.

I looked over all of them and stared in complete shock. Anger, confusion, guilt. All the emotions spread through me. For under the blanket, was my dead body.

Sofia Botnari (12)

Terrified!

I heard a noise behind me... Then I felt a cold hand touch my shoulder. My skin was shivering, the doors were slamming, the floor was creaking, my heart was exploding. Suddenly, the world stopped. I couldn't move, I felt numb. I was forced to turn around, then I saw the most horrific creature in the entire world...

Red demonic eyes, teeth like swords, a green warty face with gloopy saliva, thin arms and feet, with a ripped shirt and shorts. I also noticed a broken chain on his neck. I tried to scream but I just couldn't. I fell to the floor as the monster approached me with great anger. He was massive compared to me, at least two times bigger. I decided to run! I ran up the stairs and hid in one of the rooms of the mansion and closed the door. Slow but heavy footsteps echoed up the stairs as I quickly hid under the bed. I felt petrified. Then the door opened. There was nowhere to hide, he had seen me...

I walked backwards until I touched the wall. The monster approached and lifted me up and... hugged me! I was as surprised as you are. I was so relieved. It turns out he was friendly and hadn't seen anyone in years.

With that, I backed off and ran out of the mansion. Then I found out that it was abandoned. For the next few days, I didn't say a word about it...

Sohayb El Hana (10)

Asa's Story

I slowly crept out of bed and entered the cluttered kitchen. Dirt covered the floor and I was trying to avoid stepping in it as I made my way to the apartment steps. All I could hear were sirens, shouting and talking. I opened the brown front door and started walking down the staircase to the flat's entrance. It felt like forever since I had been anywhere except my stepdad's apartment. He had forced me to stay cooped up in there for a long time - I never knew why though.

I finally stepped down the last step of the staircase and braced myself. I gripped my hands on the handles of the two glass double doors. All I saw were blue and red flashing lights, I wanted to know what was going on. I slowly opened the doors and stepped into the cold breeze. I immediately saw a police officer and ran over to her.

"What's going on?" I asked, confused and frustrated.

"It's Jason Lightfoot's son!" someone shouted through the sirens and talking. The whole world seemed to fall silent and all that was left was the repetitive sound of sirens.

"I think it's best if we tell you in the morning," the female police officer softly muttered.

I slowly ascended back up the steps, crying, and mumbling to myself, "It's going to be okay, Asa, it's going to be okay." I opened the brown door once again, entered the flat, and sprinted to my bedroom. Tears streamed down my face. I slowly drifted off to sleep.

Knock, knock. Someone was at the door. I carefully dodged the rubbish on the kitchen floor and opened it. I saw a policeman with a look of seriousness on his face. Last night's memories came flooding back to my head.

112

"Hello, I'm here regarding the events of last night," he said in a deep, gruff voice.

I ushered him in and asked, "What happened?"

He sighed and started, "As you probably know, your dad..."

"Stepdad," I interrupted.

"Oh yes, stepdad, he went out with his friends last night. He was caught shouting at a few people and ganging up on them. We separated them but your stepdad refused to back off. We had to call another unit in. But to escape being arrested he... he-"

I was speechless. I knew he had been involved in previous police incidents, but not this big, and now he was gone. Like all the rest of my family. *I guess it'll be me next*, I thought.

"We will have to find a relative for you to live with, but if we can't, you will be put up for adoption."

Deep inside, I hoped that they would find a member of my family I never knew about. But I couldn't help thinking about what the possibilities would be if they didn't. I heard heavy breathing and looked up. The police officer was still there, I'd forgotten.

"You can go now if you want," I said to the officer.

"I'm afraid I can't leave you home alone," he said, "even if you want to stay here."

"What, why?"

"It's against the law."

"Well, why did my stepdad break the law then?" I shouted, surprised at how loud I was. The police officer went silent and gave me a sympathetic look. Suddenly, I heard another knock on the door.

"That's Julie, she'll be looking after you while we try to find you a relative. She very kindly volunteered herself. I'll go get the door," he explained.

I sat alone on the sofa, not uttering a single word until Julie came in. *Wow, not even a bye from the officer,* I thought to myself.

"Hi, I'm Julie, I've come to look after you while they find you a relative - it usually takes a day or so!" she exclaimed in a cheery, happy voice while smiling.

I felt sick. *I don't want to live with this lady for ages,* I thought. It was nearing lunchtime, so I went into the kitchen. The floor was sparkling.

"Julie, what did you do with the dirt?" I asked, angry and upset.

"I vacuumed it up, of course!" she replied in the same joyful voice.

"Nooo, those were all my stepdad's possessions!" I said.

I knew I hated my stepdad, but he was the only one I had left.

Athena Hunt (11)

Queen Elizabeth II

It all started with King Edward VIII. King Edward VIII was Princess Elizabeth's uncle. One day he just gave up the throne. No one knew who was going to be king or queen until they announced that Elizabeth's father (King George VI) was going to be crowned their next king. Elizabeth could not believe what she was hearing. She knew that when her father died she would be the next Queen.

In 1952 King George VI had fallen very ill with a disease called thrombosis. On the 6th of February 1952, they found out that he had died at the age of 56. Luckily, he did not feel much pain as he died in his sleep.

Elizabeth was sad but scared at the same time because she was becoming the Queen. She had her first children, Prince Charles and Princess Anne, before she was Queen. By the age of 37, she had all of her children, Charles, Anne, Andrew and Edward.

In 1977 the Queen had her first jubilee, it was silver to mark 25 years on the throne. Over her reign, the Queen experienced her silver, golden, diamond and platinum jubilee. She had reached 96 but unfortunately, she was very ill.

On the 8th of September 2022, she sadly passed away. Her funeral was on the 19th of September 2022. This means that Prince Charles is now King Charles III.

Amellia Lufkin (9)

YoungWriters® *Est. 1991*

How Pomander Was Invented

Once upon a Tudor time, when Elizabeth I was ruling England, there was a servant called Margaret Hadfield. She did not like her job, she was in charge of cleaning the toilet, which was gross. It stank so much nobody could bear it. But first, let me tell you how she got such a terrible job. Margaret's dad used to be in charge, but once he fell into the pit so Margaret took the job after his death.

Queen Elizabeth was ruthless, but maybe she was not that bad. Because, after all, her mother was beheaded, her daddy didn't really love her and her half-sister, Mary, hated her.

Elizabeth I's likes and dislikes:

Likes:

Shakespeare plays

Giving her old stockings to her servants

Dressing up (gowns and make-up)

Dislikes:

The colour puke (dirty brown)

Toilets (in Tudor times, toilets weren't pleasant, it was a bench with a pit and every two days they would stink. Eeeeew!)

So, Elizabeth I liked to give her stinky stockings to her servants as a present. Well, that's exactly what happened to Margaret. One day, she finished another hard day at work and she heard something about the Queen giving Christmas presents. This year was Margaret's first full year at work, so she didn't know what was going to be the present, she felt excited.

When she went to her room for a good night's sleep, she was called to go to the Queen. She was scared and thought *have I done something wrong? Why is she calling me?* When she got to the Queen on her throne, there was a basket next to her. Margaret had never been in the palace at night before, it was dark, only one candle in front of her. It was looming as if a monster was about to jump at her... When it was her turn to talk to the Queen, the Queen herself bent down to get something in the basket and gave it to terrified Margaret. She gazed upon her hand as if it was her only hope and turned her head unpleasantly. It was smellier than expired milk and cheese, rotten meat, troll's feet and Gangster Granny's cabbage soup all combined. It was Elizabeth's stockings.

"You must not throw away these stockings, you have to put them by your bed and smell them with pleasure, understand?" she shouted.

Margaret hurried to her room and put the stockings next to her bed and sighed deeply. "What am I going to do?"

The next day, when she was going to empty the toilet in the landfill, she saw some herbs growing in the forest. Margaret smelled them and the sweet herbal smell blocked the toilet smell. It smelled nicer than freshly baked cookies, it was cinnamon. *Could I take it back with me? I could pop them up in my sleeves* Margaret thought. So she decided to take them back. She scurried to her room and placed it next to the stockings.

Her room was as bare as a bald head, made of stone bricks. There was a tiny table made by Margaret's Uncle Mathew as a present. Unlike the Queen's soft mattress, Margaret had a hard wooden bed, which gave her the worst sore on her back and she had to wake every morning with a wave of revolting stocking smell.

That night, after another hard day at work by the toilet, she fell fast asleep. The next morning, she realised she had had the best sleep ever because of the smell of the sweet cinnamon. *Wow, this is lovely, I should get some more!* she thought. *Next Tuesday I have to empty the toilet again, maybe I'll rip off a piece of cloth from my dress, wrap the herb then tie it with some straws.*

Since then, she tried many different herbs and told the other servants. Soon, everybody had it to cover up smells from smelly stockings to poor hygiene.

There was a French servant whose name was Marine, she liked to collect tree resin from the woods for her herbs. When she was making it, she saw the bundle looked like an apple and smelled like resin and amber, then she thought of a perfect name in French; 'pomme' means apple, 'ambre' means amber.

"Eureka! Pomme d'ambre!"

She told everybody and later on, it was changed to 'pomander' to be easily pronounced in English.

That is how the pomander was invented.

Zoe Tsitouridis (8)

Queen Elizabeth II

Dear Diary,

On September 8th, the royal family announced the devastating news that Queen Elizabeth II had sadly passed away. Queen Elizabeth II had passed away at Balmoral Castle in Aberdeenshire, which is in Scotland. She died at the age of 96.

Our Queen was the longest-reigning monarch ever to exist in Great Britain. Her full name was Elizabeth Alexandra Mary. Here is one of the famous quotes Queen Elizabeth II said, "I declare before you all, that my life, whether it be long or short, shall be devoted to your service and the service of our great imperial family, which we all belong." Elizabeth was crowned Queen Elizabeth II on June the 2nd, 1953, in Westminster Abbey at the age of 25.

Queen Elizabeth II gave up her life to be our Queen. We would not be here where we are right now without our amazing, hard-working Queen. The Queen let people outside of her country live in her country. Our Majesty was the head of Jamaica, Australia, New Zealand, Canada, The Bahamas and many more over the years.

Our Majesty will never be forgotten. Our longest ever reigning monarch will always be so special to the United Kingdom and other countries.

May she rest in peace. 1926-2022.

Oriel Coulibaly (11)

The London Eye Experience

During the extremely long wait in the queue, rain furiously pounded on my spotty umbrella, washing away the dust that had gathered over time. The creeping queue was bum-numbingly boring, making me agitated, and I fidgeted with the button on the side of my scruffy old jeans.

In every direction, I could hear the usual hustle and bustle of London, the animated conversation running for miles, and the footsteps of people hurrying through the driving rain. Big Ben struck 8pm as I waited impatiently. Then, my little brother bit my mum's thumb and my sister messaged her friends as a plane roared across the sky, on its way to Heathrow Airport.

Finally, it was my turn to get on the Eye. As I stepped onto the shiny, metallic floor my sister pushed me aside, chasing Reggie (my brother) because he had her phone. Eventually, I managed to take a look around and I was astonished to find how beautiful the pod looked, futuristic almost. Suddenly, the doors clicked shut and I took my seat as the Eye began to creep forward. "This is amazing," I breathed. After a little while, the metallic pod reached the highest point of the Eye. While it stopped for a few minutes I took the time to point out the many landmarks around London. The Shard, Big Ben, London Zoo, Buckingham Palace. After this, I looked below seeing everything I could. I soon noticed that our little Ford looked the size of a stag beetle that I saw on holiday. Suddenly, I heard a clunking noise from the next pod and I turned my head to see a baby wailing and their mum trying to comfort them.

As the Eye started moving, I saw the oh-so-recognisable Number 10 Downing Street standing proudly like Simba on Pride Rock. Buckingham Palace wore its jewels modestly as we floated by. Big Ben looked down joyfully on all its admirers.

All of a sudden, the ride jolted forward, and without realising, Reggie (who had been running around shouting "I'm in the supercar") fell flat on his face. Cammy (my older sister) laughed and shrieked, "I can't believe I got that on camera," but I rushed to help him.

Mum was talking to the lady next to her about politics and did not notice till he started crying. "Camilla Parks, we do not behave like that in this family!" said Mum, outraged. I could tell Cammy felt bad because she sheepishly turned her guilty face towards the window.

Then a crackly woman's voice could be heard over the loudspeaker. "Please turn to the left corner of the pod and smile for your souvenir photo," it spoke. So, we pulled a silly face to the camera and took our seats one last time.

"Please get ready to leave the London Eye Experience," came the voice again.

A couple of minutes later I gloomily trudged towards the metal, automatic doors, noticing the relieved look on my sister's face. "It was such a short ride," I murmured miserably.

Saddened, I heard the upsetting click of the shiny, metallic doors that told me the ride was over. I took one last glance at the futuristic pod and wandered out.

Mum laughed and called me "Wander Woman" as she stopped me from crashing into the pod wall.

Reggie squealed and shouted, "Again, again, again."

As we scurried out Cammy bolted past us and stood on the path, silently, waiting for us. Before we joined her, we went and collected our souvenir photo.

"Look, there's us." I pointed out excitedly.

"Me too?" Reggie asked innocently, grabbing my hand.

"Yes Reggie, darling," Mum answered fondly.

Finally, we joined Cammy on the path and we started walking to the car. I noticed my sister was holding her stomach in pain. I slipped my hand into the crook of her elbow and she whispered, "Shove off, Charlotte," but let me leave my hand there.

"Again, again," Reggie whined mournfully as he jumped in puddles with his Peppa Pig boots.

We walked for some time, listening to Mum idly chatting about work and suddenly Reggie shouted, "Carry! Carry!" so I hauled him up onto my shoulders and carried him the rest of the way.

Libby Blain (11)

The Deserted Stable Block

Sunset began and the mist swallowed the sun making it pitch-dark. As I crawled through the abandoned fields, I saw a creepy stable. There were tangling vines sprouting everywhere and broken fences leaning, with bugs scavenging over them!

I explored a bit more and realised the roof had collapsed. It had charred, crumbling trees set in the stained wooden boards, with dry yellow grass laying on hills of soil. The leaves rustled as though whispering an eternity of secrets! Wooden pillars were tangling themselves in crevices in the pale walls.

Suddenly, a broken door shut with a *slam!* As I peeked behind it, I spotted a white horse in the cramped corner of the room. It came closer and closer and tilted its head back as it looked at me. "Do you want me to ride you home?" I said. The horse nodded with joy when a picture fell to the ground, so we stumbled out of the creepiness as the stables groaned!

The moon sank beneath the stable, shooting rays of colour into the sunrise, while flowers danced, and the grass waved at me!

After a while, the sugar-blanketing white horse and I travelled home, and when I got home, a sense of relief filled me!

Hugo Barra (11)

Help, I'm Trapped In A Story

Day 1:
22:48
I've been trapped in this book for what feels like forever. It's been rough, travelling from page to page with only my small lunch to console me. The sun's beating down on me, making me dizzy, but that's the least of my worries right now. As luck would have it, I've stumbled upon a cold, dirty cave. But I'm trying to be positive, so let's call it a comfy place to rest. Will hopefully be out by afternoon tomorrow.

Day 2:
16:57
I'm not close to getting out. I'm out of food. I'm out of water and running on 4 hours of sleep. I've completely given up hope of ever getting out, but I'm going to push onward. I haven't got anyone waiting for me, or a home to go back to, but it's better living out there than starving in here. I'll keep going.

Day 3:
08:25
For the first time I've been trapped here, I finally feel there might be a little hope of escaping! I've found not just food, but water as well! Not much, but enough to last me at least 4 days, a week if I ration it. At last things are looking up in this word prison. I might stand a small chance of survival. A tiny, tiny, tiny chance.

Day 4:
13:26
I'm trying not to get my hopes up - but I think I might've found a way out, and one that's almost plausible with that! I'm going to wait a bit to gather more supplies because I don't have a clue what could be waiting. I'll get all the basics, a sharp stone, enough food and water for a few days, and something to give off light. Maybe I'll be out by the end of the week.

Day 5:
05:54
I've not gotten any sleep, I was too busy gathering supplies, and it's paid off. I've found enough supplies to last for a very long time, almost a month. I hopefully won't need them though; I've got a plan to escape. I found a rip on the front cover of the book yesterday, not huge, but just big enough to fit through, with a few minor adjustments.
I'll try tomorrow though, I'm so tired, and I need rest.

Day 6:
7:45
I've escaped, but there's a major problem. There's a huge desert surrounding me that looks like it goes for hundreds of miles. I'd be doomed, but I have all those supplies, and after all this work, I'm not going to give up. It does make sense why the sun was so hot though. That's one mystery sorted out of an assortment, I guess.

Day 7:
Lost track of time.
I must be hallucinating, or do I really see the faded silhouette of a town in the far distance? Is this it? My saviour? I'll keep walking toward it, it's the only hope I have really! I do have plenty of food left, but the berries are starting to grow mould, and the water is stale. I'll just have to deal with it.

Day 8:
Ditto.
I wasn't hallucinating! I can see the town much clearer now; I'm getting so close! I can almost taste fresh, delicious food and the cool, clear water. I must stop thinking about it, I don't want to be hungrier than I already am. I'm covered in sand from tripping over, but that's probably what I should've expected. I am in a desert after all.

Day 9:
10:59
I'm in the town! It was great to see faces of real people again, not just characters in a book. The food, the water, the people, everything was amazing! The town has a weird name that I can't pronounce, but I can spell it. It's called Chuwaeru, and I love it!
I found somewhere comfy to sleep, and I think I'll stay here for some time until I can gather up the courage to walk the 476 miles home. I'll probably just take a plane.

I guess I don't need to keep writing this anymore. It was just a way of keeping track of the time and date. So, I guess what I'm trying to say is...
The End.

Alice Caunt (11)

The Space Hotel

Chapter One

"Space hotel!" I shouted.

"Romina, keep it down!" said my mum.

We had just arrived at the landing platform for the spaceship. If you're living in space, you've got to put it somewhere.

"I would shout the same thing if I weren't so sensible," said my twin, Romona.

"Shut up!" I said, rather annoyed.

"I have."

"Let's just get in!" said Mum, sounding a little mad.

The inside was luxurious. If this was the front desk, I couldn't wait to see the bedrooms!

"You're in room 58A," said the receptionist, handing Mum the key.

When we got upstairs to room 58A, it was more of a house than a room. Golden pillows and sculptures were scattered across the room/house.

"There's a buffet!" I said, excited.

"And a zero gravity button!" said Romona, mirroring my happiness.

"Heh heh, I paid £40,000 for this," shouted my mum.

"There's Paramount+," I said.

"Bribing works," said my mum.

"Let's call Dad," I suggested.

Our dad was at work but he would finish on Friday. We called him.

"Hi everyone!" he said.

"Hi!" me and Romona shouted.

"How are you doing?" Romona asked.

"I am feeling okay but I've gotta go. I've got a meeting with the council," he answered.

"Okay then, bye!" we all shouted.

"Bye!" he said.

The call ended.

Chapter Two: Blueberry Milkshake

"I think we should eat," said Romona after a series of rather impressive tummy rumbles came out of her.

I snorted. "Easy for you to say," I said bitterly.

"Suit yourself," she said tauntingly.

I decided I might have a snack so I went over to the buffet bit. There was everything. Eggs, bacon, bread, chicken, cereal, Jollof, dumplings, plantain, sausages, pies; you name it, they had it. I took a blueberry milkshake. It fizzed and bubbled suspiciously.

"Whatever is in this milkshake is trying to escape," I said, watching it bubble. "Wanna watch a film?" I questioned.

"Would I!" she said.

The TV was 45,120 inches long so the screen was quite large. I grabbed us each some popcorn (sweet 'n' salty) and pressed play.

"Romina! Romina!"

"Romona?" I said drearily.

"You fell asleep into your popcorn," she said.

"What's the time?" I shouted, sitting up quickly.

"It's 7 in the morning," she answered. "I saved you some eggs and bacon. Want some?" she queried.

"Thanks," I said gratefully.

I really do have the best life.

Chapter Three: "You're Nine Years Old, Sister!"

We had just woken up from our slumber and I had got the buffet table ready way too early.

"Romina, it's way too early," groaned Romona.

"You play Fortnite at 7 o'clock in the morning," I grumbled. "You're nine years old, sister!"

"Fine, I'll have a bit," said Romona quietly.

I took three sausages and she took some bacon.

"I was thinking of going on a water slide," said Romona.

"Sounds cool," I said, excitedly.

We woke Mum up and asked her. "Fine, go on to the park. Have fun!" she called sleepily.

We both giggled. The water slides were amazing. We sped down one called Maiden's Broom. It went up and down.

Exhausted and hungry, we ate lunch at the snack bar. I had five chilli dogs. Romona looked impressed. "How did you eat all those?" she asked, surprised.

"You can never have too many chilli dogs," I joked.

It was the best day.

Elana Branker-Olojugba (9)

Spy Banana And The Black Hole Beast

There was a big, black, dark hole and in it was a hideous, dark monster. It sometimes came out and destroyed everything it saw. But there was one hero who could stop this beast... Spy Banana! I am Spy Banana and I went to look for the beast and found a village on the way.

There was a choice, two drinks. One was purple, the other was yellow. I, Spy Banana, chose yellow. I drank it. I then went for weapons. I chose a blade, an axe and a shield. Now for armour. A helmet, a chest cast and iron shoes.

I was just walking away, but then I could see the dragon! I said, "Oh, a dragon black hole... Wait! The Beast!"

It shot a purple fire at me. I didn't feel anything though, so I shot it and it flew away. A village was set on fire. I got water. I threw it but everyone had become like purple ice cubes.

I was in fear but I carried on. I could see a purple and black hole. Then suddenly, a hand grabbed me and pulled me into the portal. It was The Beast! I threw my sword at it. It threw me down but then I turned super powerful! I killed him! And that is how I saved the galaxy from the Black Hole Beast!

Charlie Percival (9)

Lost In An Adventure

One sunny day, Yuna, a teen who was getting ready for her first day at school, decided that she and her friends would go for an exciting adventure on Friday after school. Just as she was texting she felt anxious that she wouldn't make any new friends, but that was just her brain. A few minutes later, her friends, Autumn, Hazel, Arianna, Sage and Lana, all replied with a yes. They were all up for a phenomenal adventure! Lana and her brother Alex were still getting ready for school, everyone else already came. Lana had finally arrived after dropping her brother. "Hey, guys!" Lana spoke.

"Hey, it feels awkward without Angela," Arianna moaned.

"So true," Lana answered. "Arianna, what are they doing in that corner?" Lana whispered.

"Oh, they are just signing up for the fashion competition, you win a trip to Spain. That's why I did it, otherwise, I do not care! I already did, you should too!" Arianna explained. Lana excitedly pushed everyone out of the way and ran to sign up.

Yuna was jogging home when she received an email that she'd entered the competition and all of her friends did too! They were all in a group of 9 children; she hoped to win. Since it was Friday, she texted her friends to see if they were ready. They were waiting in the forest.

She finally arrived. As they were walking through the dimly lit forest, they noticed it was midnight. "Um, let's go back, it's late," Hazel cried.

"Hazel, we all are staying," Autumn angrily whispered.

"Fine," Hazel replied.

While they were wandering in the forest, Sage thought she sensed something walking behind her. A few seconds later, the trees parted, making way for an ominous entity with great rows of spiralling teeth sharper than a spear.

Autumn opened her mouth to scream, but no noise came out. The monster pounced on her, the ghost of her last expression etched on her face. However, nobody had noticed, for they had already fled from whatever it was. She had passed out.

Autumn woke up in another dimension, a crimson-red sky with raging black clouds and roaring thunder. She was strapped to a tree made of tentacles in the middle of the ocean. She saw the portal which she could escape from. Her body was there and so were her friends.

Autumn swiftly ripped the tentacles and swam as fast as she could to the portal. She did not see the tentacles following her under the unusual black water of the ocean. Just as she was about to escape through the portal, the blood-red tentacles pulled her back.

She sliced them. Autumn swam to the portal and leapt through. She had finally escaped. Her friends were so worried she wouldn't make it but she did.

"Oh my god, Autumn! What happened!?" Sage cried.

"I thought you were dead. There was this petrifying dark liquid coming from your eyes, they were fully black," Lana replied with her eyes full of tears.

"I was in this other dimension, it was so crazy. The ocean was black, the sky was red. I was in the middle of the ocean tied to a tentacle tree. Luckily I escaped!" Autumn moaned.

"Let's just finish our competition and forget about this!" Hazel informed them.

A few weeks later, they had finally handed in their work. Their mannequins were beautiful, butterflies surrounded them and sparkles bordered their designs.

"We are going to win!" Yuna screamed.

After a day, the results had been handed out. There was a tie between all three teams! They all won a lovely trip to Spain!

"Yes!" Yuna screamed as she found out.

"I don't even care, that is so lame," Autumn whispered.

"Excuse me, be quiet and I know, because we get the trip to Spain that's literally the reason we did it!" They all screamed angrily.

Ibtihaal Kamraan (9)

Dear Hermione Granger

Dear Hermione Granger,

I am writing to inform you that you are invited to my Hogwarts-themed dinner party. The party will be held in the dinner hall of Hogwarts castle on Sunday 25th of September 2022. The reason I am inviting you is because I admire your acting skills. I love how you execute your spell casting and protect your friends.

When you arrive at the party, I would like to ask you, "How did you feel when you punched Draco Malfoy?" and "What is your favourite spell?" After, can you teach me some spells, please?

We will eat some treats from Honeydukes/Weasley's Wizard Wheezes and maybe eat some appetizers.

I almost forgot the party is at 5 in the afternoon. There will be loads of guests and maybe some of your professors. Since reading your book, I have been inspired by you to practice some spell casting so I can be just like you.

I need to go now because I need to prepare for the party next Sunday. I will be delighted and honoured if you will accept my invitation. Hope you will be there.

From,

Keanne Botin.

Keanne Botin (10)

YoungWriters®
— Est. 1991 —

Waiting...

When is she going to come? When?
I stared up at the clock and sat down, each little golden hand ticking like a bomb by the oakwood numbers.
The clock hung on a wall that was the colour of what I had heard the ocean looked like. That was all there was though. It was so lonely, and the ticks were so flat, so painfully monotonous.
Huh? Almost like it was incessant.
Every second felt like an hour, every minute felt like a day; to conciliate myself, I tried to imagine what it would be like meeting her. I vaguely remembered her, when she held my hand and taught me to walk along the deserted pier.
I remembered her long, luscious, brown, silky hair cascading in the wind and her dark green, cat-like eyes when she looked down at me; anyone could have gotten lost in them.
I began tiptoeing down the corridor, walking past the copious number of restrained bookshelves and dusty frames. I gently stepped past the crepitating floorboards and reached the end of the corridor. There standing before me was a grand, ligneous door covered in intricate, iridescent silver patterns.
With a sigh, I held the handle and pushed the door adagio. Whilst the door was ajar, I paced up and down the room impatiently when I caught glimpse of a small cupboard in the corner of the room.
I intriguingly stepped in front of it and knelt. It looked like a tattered piece of china just on the verge of breaking; however, it was beautifully decorated and it looked handmade. There were paintings of ancient Greek gods and supposedly humans going to war. Despite the look of it, it was somehow graceful and elegant in the same way.

136

I gently touched the edge of it, and like a reaction, it creaked open. I expected there to be some sort of treasure or something. All there was was a mirror engraved into the china. I saw my face: *I look like her*, I thought to myself. *She left me here a long time ago, how could she?*

Then I realised I was supposed to be happy, not weeping about for no reason. I went to the window, seeing the sign of my orphanage, knowing that she was coming. I didn't know how much longer I could wait. Time was against me.

I trudged upstairs to my dorm, only to see my isolated bed in the corner of the room. I only had one item, my only item, the only thing that I had to remember. I was told that it was the only thing with me when she left me here. It was an arresting set of kachina dolls that lay on the comfort of my duvet. I guess she had a knack for collecting ornaments like that.

I flopped on my bed bored as ever and began questioning whether she was ever going to come.

I heard three loud bangs on the door, but I knew I shouldn't get my hopes up. It was probably the warden telling me off for not doing the dishes. The more and more I thought about it, the more and more I knew she wasn't going to come. I couldn't believe I spent my time believing, thinking that she was actually going to come. *Oh well. I shouldn't keep the warden waiting. I don't want to get into any more trouble than I am already.*

I sauntered down the stairs and opened the door. To my surprise, it was not the warden but a pretty puzzled-looking woman. I assumed that she was probably looking for someone to adopt. "The warden is not here at the moment," I explained. She said nothing.

She began inspecting me like I was a piece of artwork in a museum. I saw her dark green, cat-like eyes looking at me and her brown, silky hair cascading in the wind behind. She touched my cheek almost like she knew what I was thinking. It couldn't be. No. I pinched myself in disbelief. I gave in. "Mother."

Siri Puranik (11)

The Boy In A Band

There once was a young girl called Amy. Amy was 15 and she was a huge fan of the boyband 21 Forever. The youngest boy in the group, Aron, was going through a lot of problems with stalkers and stuff, so one day, he decided to run away. He disguised himself and ran but an unexpected thing happened. Aron wasn't paying attention and bumped right into Amy. Aron said sorry and quickly explained everything.

Amy took him to her hideout. Amy's mum and dad were always fighting so Amy went there to escape it all. Since Aron was in his teens, he didn't have a place to stay so Amy said he could stay in her hideout.

After a few days, word got out that Aron was missing and a huge search party started. He never got found.

But one day, someone noticed Amy went to the hideout every day so they followed her. When they got there, there was no one there.

Later that night, Amy heard a knock on her window. She looked and it was Aron. Turns out, Aron had a hidden fortune. He got all the money and wanted to run away with Amy. So they ran away together.

Cayla Churchill (10)

The Sky Ladder

Once upon a time, there was a little girl called Ivy. After breakfast, she went outside with her dog called Daisy to go for a little walk around the garden. Daisy saw a beautiful rainbow beside the garden fence. Daisy ran over to the rainbow and noticed a mysterious ladder. Ivy ran over to Daisy to see what she had run off to look at. Daisy was nervous about going up the ladder but Ivy wasn't and she ran up the ladder as fast as she could. Daisy tried to catch up with her but she couldn't find her.

"Ivy, Ivy, where are you?" barked Daisy worriedly.

Daisy climbed to the top of the ladder.

"There you are, Daisy," said Ivy. "I was wondering where you were."

"Me too," barked Daisy.

They walked past a bush.

"What are those wings peeping out of the bush?" barked Daisy. Ivy looked closely. Suddenly, three fairies popped out of the bush.

"Wow, they are fairies," gasped Ivy with delight.

"Yes, we are fairies," said one of the fairies.

"This is Crystal with the pink dress, this is Summer with the purple tiara and I am Winter," she explained.

"We need your help!" shouted Crystal. "Princess Bella is stuck in a locked up room. We need to rescue her from the castle."

"I have an idea!" said Ivy. "You can turn Daisy into a flying unicorn."

140

"Okay," said Summer.

With a ping and a poof, Daisy was a flying unicorn. The fairies gave Ivy a magical key to unlock Princess Bella's cage. Ivy hopped onto Daisy and they flew into the air to save Princess Bella.

As they reached the top of the enchanted castle, Ivy was rushing around trying to find the room where Princess Bella was captured. Ivy finally found the room that Princess Bella was trapped in.

"Hello, Princess Bella," said Ivy.

"Hello?" said Princess Bella.

"My name is Ivy and I have been asked to save you. I have a magical key to set you free," said Ivy.

"Thank you for coming to save me!" said Princess Bella.

Ivy unlocked the cage and Princess Bella hopped onto Daisy and they flew down to the castle grounds.

"Thank you for saving me," said Princess Bella. "Sadly, my friend, Evie, has been trapped in the moat by the beastly moat monster. Can you help me rescue her?"

"I know what to do," said Ivy. "We need to call for my fairy friends so they can turn me into a scuba diver and turn Daisy into a whale. That way we can rescue Evie in no time."

Ivy called for the fairies and explained about Evie. With a ping and a poof, they turned Ivy into a scuba diver and Daisy into a whale.

Ivy jumped into the water with Daisy and scooped up Evie out of the moat before the moat monster spotted them.

"Thank you," said Evie gratefully.

"You're welcome," said Ivy happily.

Ivy returned back to Daisy with the fairies.

"You have saved our kingdom," said the fairies. "Please come back again."

They turned Daisy back into a dog so that they could return home.

"I can't wait to come back," said Ivy. "Your kingdom is wonderful. Thank you for the lovely adventure. Call me if you need my help again."

Ivy and Daisy travelled back down the ladder and it disappeared into the distant sunset.

When they got home, Mummy called to tell them it was dinner time. After dinner, Ivy couldn't wait to go to bed so she could sneakily write the magical fairy adventure into her journal so she always had the memories to read back on. That night, Ivy dreamt of the adventures that were awaiting her.

Emily Jenkins (7)

My Trip To Slovakia

First, we got up in the middle of the night. My daddy got the cold water out of the water bottle then he boiled the kettle and then drove a long way.

When we reached Birmingham Airport the wind started to blow. The plane blasted up. We went on a 737 Ryan Air. I was looking down at the snowy houses in Slovakia.

We got to Slovakia. Grandad was happy to see me. It was snowing. I was extremely happy. In the room, a mouse was eating our chocolate. We put a mousetrap in the room. We were sleepy and went to bed.

We got up in the morning. I was dreaming and Mummy got up early in the morning. I was still asleep.

I played outside. I fell down. Then my hands were freezing. I put my hands near the furnace. My mummy made me some food. I saw it snowing. My mummy was so happy she made up a song saying "It's snowing, it's whitening, the old man is singing because it was grandad and he was very happy."

We built a snowman but it kept breaking.

The next day Grandad came to visit us. We all went on a bus.

Ross Parker (6)

The Robot's Life

It was a sparkling, magical night.
Hi there, I'm Darcy the robot. I am the funniest, cleverest robot ever! You see, I'm not like any other robot. I'm a robot that can sing, dance, be invisible, talk and tell the best jokes! I can do all of this because I have an important arm. That important arm is used for teleporting, robot voices, travelling and stuff. I'm right now looking for a house. Eagerly I've been searching all through Europe.
Anyway, last week something really weird happened... The curtain of streaming stardust tickled my metal head as I walked up to a shiny, white, cute, little house. So I quietly stepped inside and said, "WOW." I heard a toothbrush banging on the sink and a tap running. *Woah, woah, woah. I shouldn't be looking around*, I thought. *There's someone in this house!* It was crazy, so in my panic, I hid behind the sofa and frantically hit one of my buttons. Okay, okay, I made myself invisible but at least I could continue to explore the house.
I cautiously crept up the stairs, careful not to make any noise so I didn't blow my cover. And wow! Stunned, my jaw dropped like a pebble being thrown into the sea. A whole robot bedroom, with movies and paintings and everything! *Hmm, interesting, whoever's bedroom this is must really love robots. I mean who wouldn't? We are calm and funny and the best friends anyone could ask for.* I decided this would be the best place for me to put my stuff and so I placed it down by the bed and made myself visible again.

Immediately a great lightning strike shot past with a starry, magical message: 'come back Darcy'. Uhhh ohhh, it was too late. A small figure appeared in the doorway. A young girl gasped in surprise. "OMG! You're a robot!" screamed the girl.

So, to cut a long story short, this little girl (her name was Clemmie by the way) would not stop talking and asking questions but soon enough it felt like we had known each other forever, and we soon began our adventures together. We travelled to beaches, beautiful tall cities, and green leafy forests when all of a sudden, whilst deep in the Amazon, disaster struck... My teleportation button broke! Initially, we felt worried and scared. We searched tirelessly to try and find our way out of the forest. We felt the earth crunch beneath our feet with every step and saw parrots and crows swoop past us.

After hours of searching, we stumbled upon something highly surprising. A trail of shimmering, shiny gold. Clemmie said we should follow the trail, that it must lead to something, maybe even get us out of here and so we began to follow it. With our newfound hope, we played I spy and sang songs.

After about an hour of walking down the trail of gold, we saw four men in the distance, all wearing eye patches and wooden legs. Suddenly one of the men approached us and yelled, "Hello there, matey, moi name is Nile and these are moi crewmates Adie, Archy and Tom. What can we help ya with?"

Clemmie stepped forward and replied, "We are lost, stranded actually, and want to get out of here, can you help us?"

"Why of course we can." Adie smiled. "Just let us finish buryin' this treasure and you can come on our ship with us!" And that brings us to today. Clemmie and I love being with the pirates! We laugh, sing, get treasure and sail the sea. We get to watch magnificent sunrises and sunsets and it's fair to say neither of us could be happier.

Teddy Cobb (8)

The Time-Travelling Lady

At night, an old lady was woken by a dreadful storm. She sat up, looking at the cobbly path. Mounds of bricks were surrounding her little cottage. The light dimmed. While she noticed that she was in early Victorian years, buildings crowded the house whilst the lamp posts leaned away from the house as the smoke came pouring out the chimney. The dark navy blue mist surrounded the street. It was like she'd time-travelled back in time!

She went back to the bedroom as she waited until the morning. Then when it was the morning she heard birds chirping then she saw a spy. She called the police as she scrambled out of bed and he got put in jail and then she made a cup of tea. Good luck because she time-travelled back to the present.

It was an adventurous day! She couldn't wait for tomorrow for another day with adventure.

Milly Morris (8)

The Wild Reunion

Hello, I am Safiya, a rhino. I live in the wild in South Africa where the magnificent, rough and sandy red ground is walked on by not only people but herds of thousands of different species. Every day when the glorious red sun sets, the sounds of antelopes racing, cheetahs pouncing and lions roaring fade into distant memories that repeat at the next day's dawn. Every day we take a long stroll to the nearby lake with refreshing water which is as blue as the sky of the sunniest days.

Meanwhile, in England lived a young girl called Adia who came from South Africa too but she couldn't afford to visit her picturesque home country. One day, at the start of her school's summer break, she asked her parents to help her enter the Young Writers' competition.

After a few weeks, she found out that she won a free family holiday to a chosen destination for two weeks. Immediately, she chose South Africa. Her parents were delighted and packed their bags.

They were on their way when Adia found out about the rhinos - us - she found out we were becoming extinct because of the poachers.

"Mami, Tati, what are poachers?"

Her parents explained everything. She burst out in tears. How could someone harm innocent animals?

Then she wrote in her diary:

'Dear Diary,

We are on the plane to South Africa and I found out about the poachers. Now I will do all I can to stop them. I will update you on this later when I get there.

Adia'

After a few hours, she arrived. In only a few moments, she asked her parents if she could go see the animals. Of course, they agreed. Adia saw the lions, the elephants, the cheetahs and the buffalos, but none of them were as amazing as the rhinos. She adored our large horns and our rough, grey skin.

There was one rhino calf which was not as social and excited as the others. It was behind the others, but as it noticed Adia, it stood up and slowly walked over. Adia spoke to it and it spoke back. It said, "Nice to meet you, Adia. I'm Safiya." The rhino was a girl and she was me. After that, I said, "Adia, don't be afraid, please. We are all afraid of-"

"Poachers," Adia accidentally interrupted.

"Yes, poachers," I replied, "they killed my father."

"I'm sorry for your loss," Adia said.

"Thank you," I said. "Can you please come back tomorrow?"

"Definitely. In fact, I'll stay with you overnight for protection," Adia bravely announced.

"Adia, thank you very much!" I replied gratefully.

On the next day, we had a visit from a not-so-kind guest - the Poacher Chief, they called him.

I woke up quite early that day because of loud galloping and distressing screams. As I opened my eyes, I saw a net flying from the Poacher Chief's hand and it trapped me. I screamed.

Luckily Adia heard me and said to the Chief Poacher, "Morning! Can you please show me and my family the way to the town hall? What a large beautiful dog you have!" she said about me, acting that she was stupid, to gain me time.

He led Adia and her parents there to not look suspicious and the herd of rhinos managed to escape. Adia was a genius!

But one rhino couldn't escape - my mother.

Peew! The gun shot.

It hit her. I couldn't believe it. Then I burst out with the most miserable of tears.

How will I cope? What will happen...?

Maya Dworak (11)

The Fairy Friends

Once upon a time, there were two fairy friends called Elena and Arabella. They always played together and went to the fairy school together.

One day, Elena could not find Arabella. She searched for her and she found Mr Ginnybunting. Mr Ginnybunting took away Arabella's lovely house with its mesmerising garden. When Elena asked Mr Ginnybunting about Arabella, he started to get a bit snappy. Elena felt very disappointed and sad at the same time because her best friend had left and she never saw her in school.

One day, Elena decided to search for her. She got a bit tired and saw a tree. She sat down and rested beneath the tree. She closed her eyes and saw Arabella's footsteps with her vision powers, so she tried to find Arabella. Luckily, she found Arabella and they lived happily ever after.

Mishka Saxena (5)

The Alley

In the distance, I saw something that could change my life...
I normally live in the alley of the streets where people dump
their garbage. There are a lot of people in the alleys which
makes every day a fight for survival. We feed off leftovers of
our dry, crusty city, and the people are awful. So, I always
have to steal food or go to different alleys to search the
garbage bins for food.

Not only do I have to feed myself, I also have siblings and a
lot of them, however, I am the oldest. Being the oldest, a lot
of responsibilities fall into my hands. Some involve finding
food or taking care of the younger ones, sending them to
school and paying fees, and if I am not there to do all these
jobs the younger ones might suffer a lot of loss.

The city is always dry and filled with mean people. Although
I do not like the alley I still prefer to be here than to go and
face the cruel world out there. Some families who live in the
alleys get food by searching through the garbage cans,
while some who were once rich refuse to get food through
that method as they think that since they were rich, they
would rather steal to get their hands filthy.

The people are mean and that makes me want to act mean
so that I can seem tough, and I always tell my siblings to act
mean to avoid being an easy target to steal or take food
from.

Every day, two of my siblings (who are the two oldest after
me) and I go on a food hunt to different alleys.

After we search the alleys, we steal some food in case the
ones from the alleys are not enough. Each alley is more
disgusting than the other.

After the food hunt, we share the food amongst ourselves and make sure to leave a little extra food in case when we go for another food hunt there is not enough food.

One graceful day, when going on the usual food hunt - but without my siblings - I decided to steal some food first before checking the garbage bin. Stealing food was not easy, especially since I did not have my sisters to help me distract the people. While stealing, I saw a man and he was walking somewhere so I followed him hoping that I could steal something from him. He was walking into an alley so I used that chance to steal his wallet and I managed to steal it.

I then decided to search the alleys so I did not have to go back to the mean city. Alley after alley, I saw disgusting stuff, rotten food, half-eaten food, decayed food and even a lot more. I had to ignore it but it was hard because I did not have anyone to keep me company.

I searched alley after alley until I came to one particular one (it seemed hidden). In the distance, I saw something that could change my life. It was glistening so I decided to check it out.

I realised it was a gold bag and I had a huge smile on my face. I thought about how much money I could get and how I could take care of my family. I carried the bag and it felt very heavy so I decided to open it. My eyes lit up when I saw what was in the already rich-looking bag. There were a lot of coins and they were gold.

I began to think about all the things I could do with the coins... until I remembered all the homeless people out on the streets. I realised that the gold coins could not only help me but they could help so many other people.

So, I gave the money to people. Our city turned from mean to kind. After seeing the smile on the people's faces of my city, I went to other places hoping the world would change... one very day.

Iranlowooluwa Esther Akindipe (11)

The Pranksters

It was a normal day until the two troublemakers, Jason and Jake, struck again. Jason smashed a pie in his dad's face and laughed as the pie hit his face. Jake threw water balloons at his mum's face and as he did, he laughed as his mum got soaked.

"Did they get you?" asked the dad.

"Yes, can you not see he literally soaked me?"

"We have to get them back," suggested the dad.

"But how?" questioned the mum.

"We could prank them by saying there is a surprise outside, then lock them out."

"Yes, that's a great idea."

"Kids, we've got a surprise waiting outside for you!"

The kids ran outside without knowing what was coming for them. When the kids ran outside, the parents quickly locked the door on them.

Lianna Ncube (11)

Jack The Beast Warrior

We all know the story of Jack and the Beanstalk.
Nobody knows if it's faux or true,
And I'm not going to decide because the answer's up to you.
This story will take you down many twists and turns,
To a village in flames and a cemetery piled high with urns.
Now this story has never been told,
So consider yourself lucky because this tale will be
remembered till you are old.
I can tell you are very enticed and keen to read on further,
Let your eyes behold the marvellous sight,
And allow your imagination to take flight,
Now we are ready to enjoy the tale of good and evil's fight.

In a quiet village in a faraway land, a more modest kid
would soon wage war with the forces of darkness and this
boy was named Jack, otherwise known as the Giant Slayer.
"Jaaaaaack!" bellowed the loud shrill voice of his mother.
Slowly, Jack rose from his bed. He was deeply frustrated by
his mother's loud voice waking him from his slumber. He
folded his blankets and spread his duvet before slowly
getting ready for his long, tedious day.
"Morning, Mother," said Jack whilst he helped himself to
breakfast. Two small succulent sausages, some crispy bacon
sizzling on his plate, and toasted crumpets slathered in
butter. It had been two years since his adventure on the
magic beanstalk, and whilst having more money than the
last couple of years of his life, things hadn't changed.

He slowly munched on a rasher of bacon and took a small bite of his crumpet while looking at his rather plump mother with a plate piled high with eggs, bacon, sausages, pancakes and toast, shovelling them into her mouth at an incredible speed.

After he finished breakfast, he packed his satchel with a dagger, a few coins, and a sandwich for later. He looked towards the valley and noticed smoke forming in the clouds and fire in the houses below. He raced down the valley's top and stopped dead in his tracks when he saw a wolf prowling the village. He observed the creature and realised it wasn't just a wolf. It was also a man.

Jack slowly walked towards the valley; careful not to be seen, he started to run towards the beast. Dagger in hand, Jack charged at the creature. He jumped and narrowly missed. The beast had dodged and now turned to face Jack. Jack stared at the beast's vermillion bloodshot eyes with fury in his.

He leapt at the animal and swung his blade at its hairy chest. The beast clawed at Jack, desperately trying to scratch him; Jack turned his blade, retaliating. The knife sliced across his eye, temporarily blinding him whilst Jack ran to the nearest building in sight - the crematorium.

Jack looked back as he saw the beast racing after him. He quickly opened the door and bolted it before hiding behind a silk-laced curtain embroidered with the most beautiful designs of flowers. Soon, the beast ripped the door to nothing but wooden shreds as he kicked the hinges away. He prowled the area menacingly, looking for his victim. Jack cautiously peeked from behind the curtains to look. The beast's back was turned. Jack assumed this was his chance. He jumped and lunged his blade towards the spine of the beast.

He pushed it, but the beast saw out of his peripheral and punched Jack back, then pounced, but Jack was swifter, and when the beast was above him, he struck its underside and slayed the beast.

After that day, Jack was considered a hero and a Beast Warrior.

The end, for now...

Jabez Hoyte (11)

Saving Planet Earth

Do you remember how hot you felt during the heatwave? 19th July 2022 was the hottest day in the United Kingdom.

We are adding a lot of greenhouse gases to our atmosphere by burning fossil fuels, which give off carbon dioxide and other gases. Too many greenhouse gases can make the Earth warmer by trapping heat. Ice is melting and the sea level is rising. The climate is changing, there are more droughts, hurricanes and heatwaves. Animal species are dying because of wildfires.

Some of the ways we can protect the Earth are:

- Walk or cycle to places as much as possible
- Recycle glass and plastic materials
- Switch off the television and lights after use
- Throw litter in the bin.

Let's all work together to save Planet Earth!

Idris Lashkor (6)

The Wormhole

It was a bright, cloudless day. The enormous warehouse loomed over Mark Wrangell's face. He had been designing and making a technological masterpiece over the past six months, and it was finally ready. Today, he was setting the record for the fastest dodgeball in the world. The Guinness World Record officials were waiting, neutral-faced, for him. As the gate opened, Mark took a deep breath and stepped inside. When he, at last, dragged the unit of a machine in, it was apparent how intricate this was. It was a handheld particle accelerator made to speed up a 1 x 1 x 1 cm cube of exotic matter to two times the speed of light. Mark corrected the opening of it, then taped a dodgeball to it.

"Ready when you are," said the person in the middle of the group.

Mark started it up. The box of metal started whirring. It kept whirring and whirring, faster and faster. Mark's hand was hovering over the release button, and he slammed it down. *Boom!* The dodgeball vaporised the tape, broke a hole in the roof, and flew off into the distance.

"Jeez, that was some speed," Mark said to himself.

"Wow," someone muttered.

"Now, you have officially set the Guinness World Record for the fastest dodgeball ever," the head official stated, handing Mark a framed certificate.

"Yesss! Thank you!" Mark whooped.

They all slowly filed out of the warehouse. Mark was dragging the apparatus and celebrating. Suddenly, a person from the group fainted and collapsed onto the floor. The people with him stared open-mouthed at the sky, screamed, and started running towards nowhere. "Oh my god!"

Mark dropped the accelerator.

The warehouse, where Mark had his record attempt a few days ago, was teeming with people. People in white coats, people in suits of every colour, TV cameras and reporters spilling all over the place.

And in the middle of the chaos was Mark, flabbergasted. All eyes were fixated on a black, endless tunnel stretched upwards into the sky. It started roughly four storeys high, with the opening shaped like a horn.

"Apparently, your dodgeball broke space-time, effectively creating a wormhole," a scientist said to Mark.

"Nice," Mark replied vaguely.

"No, this is absolutely bonkers. You should be proud of yourself."

"Okay, sooo... what are you gonna do with it?"

"We're gonna explore it, of course."

"Um, okay," Mark said uncertainly.

"Maybe you should get some rest. It's gonna be a long day."

"Okay."

That night, Mark kept tossing and turning in bed, unable to sleep. Why did a wormhole not pop up in his tests? All these questions bounced around in his head, banging against his head.

The next day, Mark was sitting in a Bell 407, along with a pilot, of course, and four other people.

"Hi, my name is Xavier Wright." The person shook his hand. "I am the chief scientist in the research of this wormhole. It is an honour to meet you."

"Thanks," Mark said.

When they all sat down, the pilot started up the helicopter. They slowly began to rise, then started moving forwards, the audience on the ground eyeing nervously. When they were just under the entrance, Mark nodded to the pilot, who gave the thumbs up. Then, they moved up. A few seconds later, they disappeared into the tunnel, not knowing what they would find... or if they would survive.

Aprameya Ghosh (10)

Bully... Stop!

A bully is big.
A bully is bad.
Bullies are the ones that make you sad.

They may act like the leader of the place,
But that's not always the case.
They laugh at you, push you, shake you and pretend to be
your friend,
They pick on you, annoy you and drive you around the bend.
They make you feel as small as an ant,
Tease you and chase you until you pant.
Bullies beat, bash and smash until you cry, "Boohoo!"
Sitting all alone, thinking, *What can I do?*

Listen up and I'll tell you how,
To get rid of your bully right now.
Just walk away and ignore,
Soon, bullying will be a bore.
Ask a grown-up for some advice,
To turn the bully from nasty to nice.
Be brave and take a stand,
You will always have a helping hand.

Layth Abdur-Rahman (8)

Space Travel

"Only 30 seconds till take off," a woman reported, clutching a walkie-talkie closely. "3... 2... 1..."

The whole ground shook underneath her, and she knew that the rocket had taken off into space. She watched as the trees turned into broccoli and humans shrank to the size of ants. Clara stared out of her window; stars twinkled by, each one shining more than the next.

She turned around just in time to see a pencil start to rise. She knew this would happen, but she could not help feeling fascinated. That was until it poked her in the eye.

The woman was in fact travelling to a distant planet to collect information as the space centre where she trained had only just discovered it. They had warned her that she would feel sick because of decompression (the body having to adjust to the different gravity zones). She had no idea if she had been sitting in the capsule for hours or only a few minutes. On planets, years, days and even hours are different, so she had no way of knowing.

Suddenly, the capsule shuddered to a halt and a cool voice asked, "Are you receiving us? You are approaching your destination. Clara, please stay seated until we give further instructions."

Moments later, the voice added, "Please step out of the capsule, we are ready."

Buzzing with excitement, Clara walked out. Steps unfolded and she hopped down them two at a time. Then she looked up; this is what she saw...

Four moons shimmered in a single indigo sky. One was a ghostly green, two were sky blue, another deep purple, but it was the planet that took Clara's breath away.

It was covered in crystals. Red, green, and blue glittered endlessly and huge shards of rock dotted the landscape. Clara studied the one closest to her and realised that it looked like ice. But it was the type of ice that you could only find in the deepest caves. It was a kind of dark blueish-black and had bubbles and filaments captured within.

Clara noticed something else; a creature that looked like a red ant with four wings scuttled across an ice shard. She spotted three more, each one going into the same hole. *That must be their nest*, she thought.

"Clara?" It was her walkie-talkie. "Remember to report back to us once you've explored the area. We've only just discovered the planet, so there's bound to be something dangerous, valuable or both. Over."

Once Clara had explored for a few hours, she started to make her way back to the capsule. She had brought a camera to take photos and had even got good shots of each moon. She decided to bring a sample of crystal home but as she bent down to take some, the ground shook and there was a low rumbling sound.

Bubbling acid squirted into the air out of a crater and the acid started to melt the planet! Clara shrieked and scrambled to her feet, trying to run. The liquid didn't seem to be affected by gravity, so it was eating its way towards her at a quick pace. All at once, the acid just sank into the ground as if it was harmless water.

At last, she climbed into her capsule and watched the planet grow smaller and smaller. That's when it exploded. Chunks of rock catapulted in her direction. The capsule shook and she flew back home.

Emilia Wesslowski (10)

S3 - Secret Spy Squad

Chapter One: The Three Princesses
Once upon a time, there was a group of three intelligent princesses called Princess Navanshi, Princess Mishka and finally, Princess Amelia. They always used to play super spies together and their team was called Princess Spy Squad! Or they would simply draw or study to let their unstoppable inspiration grow in their spare time. They also loved to read as this inspired them the most.
They were blessed by the kind fairies of Inspiration Land! And so they had no weaknesses. In fact, they deserved it as they worked really, really hard. Oh, what good friends they were. They really proved who they really are.

Chapter Two: King Edward I
Do you know Princess Mishka, Princess Navanshi and Amelia were sisters? Well, the Secret Spy Squad's father, King Edward I, noticed his daughters were playing like spies and he got furious because he thought playing spies was not a game for princesses. They had to be gentle and elegant in their games.
"I will have them locked in their rooms separately. Ha ha ha!" said the king angrily.

Chapter Three: Locked In
Now, the princesses were stoppable as they were locked in. All they could think of was playing together, using their iPads and texting and texting and texting...
One day, they heard the news that the queen's spectacular crown, the precious gems and diamonds had been stolen! As they loved to play super spies, they could be the ones to resolve this mystery.

Princess Amelia had a unique power to jump as high as thirty feet, however, the others had forgotten their magical powers. Princess Navanshi and Princess Mishka started to replicate Princess Amelia. Suddenly, they had a brainwave and remembered their powers of invisibility and teleportation.

Chapter Four: The Thief
The thief had stolen the princess' mum's, the Queen of Braverly Land, crown. Hence, they decided to disguise themselves as an ordinary person, solve the mystery and find the thief.
The next day in the night, the Princess Spy Squad went out of the castle dressed as ordinary people from the empire. The princesses were walking around the empire and heard from the people that the thief was very greedy and always looking to steal the royal treasury.
Instantaneously, they had an idea of spreading hoax news of new royal treasure arriving at the Braverly Land's palace to nab the thief.

Chapter Five: The Trap
The princess kept the fake royal treasury in one of the chambers in the palace and decided to use Princess Navanshi's invisibility powers. Patiently, they waited for several hours for the thief to arrive.
Finally, when the thief arrived they nabbed her hand and the thief, Charlotte Robs, was successfully trapped. They used Princess Mishka's powers of teleportation to teleport the thief into the palace's dungeon.

Eventually, they teleported into their rooms. Surprisingly, the princesses' parents were waiting for them. They told them about everything and King Edward was very proud of them and said, "You shall be now known as the Secret Spy Squad!"

Navanshi Saxena (8)

Tyrannosaurus Rex!

20 feet above the ground,
Bite force of 8,000 pounds,
Groundbreaking roars very loud,
Massive feet go pound, pound, pound!

You can't escape his massive jaws,
King of all the dinosaurs,
Thrashing, slashing teeth and claws,
Gouges, gorges, gashes, gores.

He roams the plains in search of prey,
And gobbles up all the eggs they lay,
He crunches all the bones like clay,
What a tasty dinner today!

If he comes at you in the night,
It might give you a great big fright,
He'll eat you up in just one bite,
He never loses any fight.

He's a T-rex, big and mean,
He's the biggest and baddest,
On the scene,
Razor teeth squeaky clean,
If you see him coming, you'll run and scream.

T-rex
Roar!

Owen Gazzard (10)

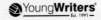
A Holiday Adventure

Chapter 1

Ring! Ring!

The school gates opened widely; everyone sprinted out of the school. Finally, school was over, it was the summer holidays. My dad had said we were going on holiday. I could hardly control my excitement.

I started walking home. I was tired after a long day of school. Luckily, my home was quite near, so it wasn't going to be a long walk. The first thing I did when I got home was lie down on the sofa. The best part of coming home. Getting to relax.

Until I was woken up by my dad yelling, "GET PACKING!"

I flew off the sofa and quickly got changed. I somehow finished packing just in time. I also decided to pack my special map my grandma made me. She always said it would take me far. I never really knew what she meant but the map was beautiful, even if not geographically correct.

As we drove to the airport, I thought about all the creatures I would see and the adventures I would go on. I started talking about all the things I was looking forward to.

Soon, we arrived at the airport; when our flight was ready, we walked onto the plane. It had red stripes and was glimmering like a ruby. We were kindly greeted by the pilot. I was so excited as this was my first time on a plane.

As we flew, I looked out of the window and I could see birds fluttering by. I wanted to ask Dad where we were, but he was extremely tired so I decided to leave him.

Finally, when we arrived, I was listening to my favourite music when the bus woke me up (where could I find peace?). Tiredly, I clambered out of the car. My mum said I would have little time to sleep but I wanted to explore.

I saw a small cave. I bravely walked into the cave, the deeper the brighter. Soon there was too much light to see but I managed to glance at a massive bridge made out of ice.

I was just about to cross it when I heard my mum shout, "Dinner time!" I dashed back to camp; I couldn't wait to explore tomorrow.

Chapter 2

I heard the worst thing in my life. When I was putting my things where they should be, I heard Tara (the school bully) was near our spot for camping. I tried to persuade my parents to leave and move somewhere else, but it was impossible. It was like trying to use a skinny stick to push a sleeping giant. I was sulking in my sleeping bag and there was nothing to do to change their minds, then it hit me.

I would just have to make Tara want to leave. I put my plan into action.

I was waiting for Tara to come. I would make her leave me alone once and for all. Soon she came, and she was drenched. Ha, my prank had gone to full success. I knew the old water bomb would work.

"Look! Queen Neptune here!" I giggled.

"You monster!" She just chased me, and my day turned out to be quite bad. Forget quite, I mean extremely bad.

When I was eating, I saw Tara taking my map. I chased her and soon we both disappeared into the heart of the forest. I was so close to her now.

"Caught you," I said to Tara. "Now give it back."
Tara looked around and saw she had no choice. She gave it back. I let out a sigh of relief. Then I suddenly noticed a second problem appearing.
Where were we?

Ifeoma Obi (7)

In The Meadow

In the meadow lie there still,
A bed of lovely daffodils;
Like little suns, and sparkly beams,
Their lofty stems
Of grassy green
Shine in the rain,
And their yellow petals glow
Like sunbeams on snow.
My heart feels glad to see them there,
When none elsewhere remain;
Their bobbing heads of yellow gold
More beautiful than daisies plain.
The wind picks up and sets them swaying,
I like to think that they are playing;
Flower and wind, wind and flower,
Dancing away the waning spring hours.
When I think of that I sigh,
I never like to see them die.
But for now, I'm glad I stumbled upon
This secret place where spring lingers on,
And I know when summer takes them away,
Forever in my mind, they'll stay.

Ruby Green (10)

A Journey To Remember

Pitch blackness draped itself like a curtain, an unleashed spirit that seemed to appear everywhere I looked, clinging to the frozen, uniformed tube as we rushed into the tunnel. I stood unflustered whilst my gaze aborted to the flickering, flaxen lights above. Stopping with ease, my eyes lingered cautiously on the fierce spotlight.

An eventual throng formed intertwining with the monotonous faces that appeared from the last stop now lost in a whirlwind of newcomers. The fragrance of oil and flaring charcoal sprits the train's sunken atmosphere overlapping with the vague pleasantries of a few passengers.

Adjusting myself to a compact corner, I felt trivial compared to the towering pedestrians who scanned the room like hawks for shrouded seats in the compartment. I pictured the train racing along the tracks, primed for a roller-coaster ride ahead to escape the everlasting darkness and slink along the smooth walls, willfully whirling with glee.

Sharp glimpses of light would intercept the awaited tunnels, bursting out from an eclipse of shadows and grappling dust in a frenzy. Unknowing yet eager, I scored the area open-minded, intaking the buffets of cold air erupting from tiny cracks and the wafting pensive of rich, plentiful perfume. The familiar pandemonium rang alarmingly to my ears whilst I considered the urge to grip the cool, burgundy pole, slim as a snake yet well sculpted.

My interior thoughts were interrupted with the undenying sound of nearby shuffling and shoving; they have no patience, an important virtue so many fail to apply accordingly. Whilst overlooked malaise glided over to my presence, I felt the curious tips of my fingers stroke the cooling metal against irregular screws, jarring and argent in both appearance and touch.

I drifted away to my world, creating a placid atmosphere for myself away from the dull and blaring reality as I whisked myself back to my hall of ideas. A common thought brushed elegantly across my mind - when would we begin our woeful journeys again?

Of course, I was not piqued but pardoned the train for long-lasting routine stops although I couldn't help feeling a tad bit vexed but alas, never mind. My twinkling eyes longed for light whilst I admired my worthy reflection in the translucent window, reflecting unevenly hung posters advertising trinkets and wasting malarky hung carefully to the dilapidated wall.

I could have sworn the paper was made to be sided with smudges and stained scum. I felt lost in this enormous world despite realising that in a place filled to the brim with people of all shapes and sizes and colours and style and appearance and behaviour, I had not found my place. Delving into my deep thoughts, I soon realised the train had begun to move at a steady pace now emerging into the flashing sun and the clear blue sky.

The newly welcomed rays of light poured through the sparkling windows whilst I sat down. Life was never expected to be entertaining but hopefully this journey was one worth taking. If only I knew what life had planned for me; well, I guess I'd just have to wait and see.

Eliza Karim (10)

Memories

Adrian was conversing with his new friend, Marcus Smith, about how he had escaped the tentacles which had invaded his city, when suddenly, a painful stab on the back of Marcus's head ignited fire in his eyes and memories that were once lost and forgotten came rushing back.

Nowhere was safe, sounds of air raid sirens drowned out any feeble attempt to scream for help. An army of colossal monsters invaded the city, surveying their surroundings and demolishing everything in their path. Even the birds were sucked out of the jet-black sky by the giant vacuums which perched on their backs - flesh-eating flames licked out of furnaces on their elongated spines. The devastation was unfathomable.

Using every ounce of their strength, a lucky couple pushed through the scalding heat and found a sewer, just large enough for them to sit in, to wait for the intoxicating dread to blow away like a leaf in the wind or a falcon in the air. "Let me help you get in. Take my hand," Marcus shouted above the ear-splitting noise.

Closing their eyes, they shut themselves out from the world and hoped that the next time they came out, they would see the majestic metropolis their city once was.

As they appeared from the depths of the ground, hoping that the apocalypse had ceased, they were met with a puzzling sight. An enormous ghost town faced them. Marcus and his wife crept round every corner, careful not to be seen by any kind of monstrous creature, for this was a place like no other; they had never seen anything like this before.

Something did not seem right to Marcus, he steadily peered round the corner and a monumental shape came into view. This meant only one thing to them. The monsters had won.

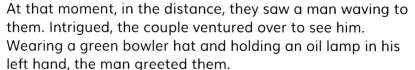

At that moment, in the distance, they saw a man waving to them. Intrigued, the couple ventured over to see him. Wearing a green bowler hat and holding an oil lamp in his left hand, the man greeted them.

"My goodness, a saviour! Please sir, can you possibly help us get out of here?" Marcus asked, worried, as he looked around tentatively.

"Sure, but I'm gonna need somin' in return," the man responded, with a grin on his face.

"We don't have anything to give you. It's all gone, look around you for goodness sake."

"Well, I got a ladder, an' yeh could give me that necklace of yours," he replied, eyes widening in greed.

"There's nothing else to do," Marcus told his wife, afraid.

"There will be other necklaces, sweetheart, but there will not be another chance like this."

"Okay, well, the deal's on!"

The strange man handed them the ladder and disappeared in the darkness, triumphant.

Relieved to be escaping this apocalypse, the couple climbed over the city walls to find a stranded boat next to the beautiful pure white beach.

"Look over there!" whispered one of them with excitement in their voice. "A boat!"

And with a last glance at their demolished city, the couple set off towards a new life - a new home.

Timeon Clarke (11)

The Competition

This story is about never giving up.

One early morning as the sun started to appear above the tall oak trees, Lucy woke up suddenly remembering that it was Monday and jumped up in excitement. Other people may not understand why she loves Mondays because children have to go to school and adults have to go to work. Lucy loves Mondays not because she gets to go to school. Lucy loves Mondays because every week, her best friend, Max, who lives on the farm just next to her farm, brings along his little brown and white pony. Max teaches Lucy how to ride because her parents can't afford the lessons that they do in the town and the next town takes one whole day to get there. So, they made a deal with Max's parents when she was three that if Lucy's parents grew an extra ten carrots on their farm and sold them to Max's parents, that they would bring their little pony called Chocolate so that Max could teach Lucy.

But one day, suddenly her mum was sitting downstairs when she woke up. She looked at her mum with a face of concern and asked her mum what was wrong. She said that her best friend Max moved away early this morning.

Lucy was so upset, she snatched the chore list off the fridge and did them all within ten minutes. Her mum didn't like seeing Lucy like this, so she pulled a leaflet out of the kitchen drawer and called the competition for young riders. She quickly rushed out to the yard to tell Lucy about the competition. She jumped up in excitement. She quickly hopped into the truck so she and her dad could set off to Somerset for the competition.

Seven hours later, they finally arrived at the competition but Lucy remembered that she had not prepared for the competition. So, she signed into the competition and found out what horse she would be riding. She found out that she would be riding a 13 hands horse and it was called Snow White which made her laugh.

She tacked up and asked her dad to help her up. She didn't have a plan, so she decided to do what Max taught her. Max had taught her how to jump using some old fences. So, she was going to do a simple height jump course because they only had tall fences that were spare from the chicken coop so she was taught how to high jump.

She finally heard her name being called out on the loudspeaker. She slowly walked out into the paddock and started to perform her routine from the farm. She heard the crowd cheering from the stands at her amazing performance.

She left the paddock feeling so happy and feeling like she had achieved something.

Her dad hugged her in joy and said he knew she would do well. As he let Lucy out of his grasp, the loudspeaker went off again and it said that now they had seen all of the riders' performances they had concluded that the winner was Lucy. She was so happy she could leap for joy. Lucy went to claim her trophy and got back into the car feeling so happy like she had achieved something better than ever.

Freya O'Dell (10)

A Silent Night

A silent night. The moist, humid air. A small boat, resting in the ocean. A black murky mist swept over the sky, causing all men on board to suddenly shiver in the newly found darkness. A deafening rumble of thunder shook the men to life. Rain started to gently pour; it started off as a quiet drip, drip, drip, rolling from the mast and landing on the crowded, muddy deck below. A luminous light sliced through the powering clouds, only just missing the boat.

"Men, we need to set sail, the storm won't be too far away!" yelled a gruff voice.

The rain grew stronger, pelting down, causing great commotion. The murky water became rougher, slapping the boat with its powerful hands. The cacophonous sound of the roaring thunder rang painfully, echoing through all ears which heard.

"We are in great danger! It will not be long until this boat can't take it anymore. We need to start sailing!" came the unmistakable voice of the captain.

"Sir, I'm sorry to say this but, well-" He paused, knowing what he had to say would not please the captain.

"Oh, spit it out, boy!" he answered impatiently. "I don't know if it's clear enough for you, but we don't have long! Grab the oars and go!"

The man was hesitant, but he knew he had no choice but to tell the captain.

"Well sir, that's the thing. The oars - they've snapped!"

Chaos rose again. The thunder was deafening, the lightning was blinding and the sea was deadly.

It was only just occurring to them that they were trapped by the raging monster. As the thunderous rumbles and the flashes of lightning struck the sea, an electrical green wave shot underneath the boat, furiously tossing it around. Suddenly, a colossal wave - as big as a mountain - ravenously gobbled them up and spat them back out again. A humongous thud smashed onto the weak deck, causing the men to be flung to the bow. The mast. It had fallen. "Man overboard!" yelled a distant voice.

Each man was frantically trying to help, throwing the longest rope over they could find, causing the angry sea to become infuriated. Then an astronomical wave consumed the man. A large puddle of blood had seeped from under the mast. A man had been crushed. Caught up in the chaos, they had no time to grab onto the boat. The only thing left to do now was pray.

Not long after, the raging beast had everyone in its wrath. Only a few seconds later its unfortunate prey was nowhere to be seen.

Somebody suddenly arose from the water, but a remaining plank from the boat struck him ferociously on the head. The silent night. The moist humid air. A growl of thunder and a crackle of lightning. The remains of a once sailing ship, slowly drifting away.

A once silent night.

Freya Mitchell (11)

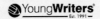

Jessica's Persuasive Letter

Ursula von der Leyen
Post Office Box 1049
Rue de la Loi 200
Belgium

Monday 4th July 2022

Dear Ursula von der Leyen,

My name is Jessica and I am in Year 4 at Featherstone Primary School. Throughout the past few weeks, we have been learning about the cruelty to animals in circuses and how animals should be banned from them. I am writing to you today to persuade you to make it illegal for travelling circuses to include animals in their performances.

The English government banned the use of animals in circuses and now there are many happier animals in our country. If you agree to do the same in Belgium, then hopefully this will influence many other countries and all animals will have the life they deserve in their natural habitats.

My first reason for wanting to set animals free from circuses is because of the barbaric training methods used. As a result of this, animals become weaker and die early. The worst thing is that animals are beaten and forced to perform. Common training methods include yelling and using electric shocks, whips and the dreaded bull hook. Imagine being poked and hit with a sharp metal-tipped stick just because you did not understand somebody. It is just cruel and unfair. There is no justice.

This is *not* how *animals* should be *treated!*
This is *not* how *anyone* should be *treated!*
This is such a *disgrace!*
Disgrace and *disappointment!*

Additionally, the crowds, bright lights, loud noises and constant travelling are confusing and stressful to these animals. For this reason, circuses are no fun for them. It is the truth! Dangerously loud noises can make them deaf while the bright lights can blind them. Think about it: just because someone might want to run away and join the circus, do you not think that elephants would rather bathe in the river, that the tigers would rather lie in the shade and that the monkeys would rather cuddle their babies and hang out in the trees?

My last argument is that circus animals live in poor conditions. When they are not performing, elephants in circuses are often chained up for long hours on hard surfaces. Bears, tigers, chimpanzees and other animals are also controlled through fear and physical abuse in overheated conditions. The trucks are badly maintained and lack the basic comforts animals need to be happy and healthy. The nimble, raucous tigers jumping through the scorching, miniature fire hoop whimper and dream for a better life.

In conclusion, animals are majestic, beautiful and whimsical but are still treated in a bad manner. I hope you consider my arguments and stop the use of animals at circuses.

Yours sincerely,
Jessica

Jessica Asiedu (9)

I'm Ready...

I'm ready to venture into this world,
To travel beyond the horizon.
To breathe in a new sensation,
To feel my mindset widen.
I'm ready...

I'm ready to be in sync with my mind,
To let my heart be my guide.
To feel that warm feeling in my body,
To relax and enjoy the ride.
I'm ready...

I'm ready to board my choice of travel,
To feel my stress slowly sink.
To be like the birds that roam the skies,
To live without a care to think.
I'm ready...

I'm ready to live life to its fullest,
To have the same aim as these strangers.
To have the privilege to explore,
To be far from familiar dangers.
I'm ready...

Abdalmonem Elber (11)

The Night Prowler

All was quiet. The trees' gentle whispering had finally quietened down, all the humans had gone to bed. Even the birds had stopped singing their melodic tunes. It was as if the whole village was holding its breath.

This silence was broken by a creaking door. Then nothing at all. A single, lithe shape slunk through a hole in a fence, then turned and made its way along a spiralling path. She crept in silence along a road, wrinkling her velvet nose at the rank stench of the cars. She swallowed, and nosed her way through a bush, grateful for the fresh, clean air of the forest on the other side. She strode confidently through the trees as though she had done it many times before. Her paw steps were silent, her blazing green eyes alight with freedom. Her muscles rippled under her death-black fur. Then, she leapt gracefully onto the tree stump, and sat, with her sleek tail wrapped around her paws. She peered through the surrounding trees, her ears twitching, her whiskers quivering. Suddenly, a heavy weight landed on top of her! She knew exactly who it was. She purred, rolling onto her back and flipping off her sister. Of course, Moon had followed her. The two young cats twined tails, their heads together. Then, Moon let out a playful chirrup and scampered through the trees. Star sighed, wiggled her haunches, and sprung!

Immediately, Star felt exhilaration spread from her nose to tail tip. She pounded after her sister, her whiskers and ears flat, her eyes slitted, and her tail streaming out behind her. Everything went past in a blur: the trees, the field, the flowers, the lake. Star knew that in that moment, she could do anything she wanted.

Finally, she skidded to a stop. Moon was crouching on the branch of a tree, her sides heaving as she recovered her breath. Then she caught sight of Star and a purr rumbled in her throat.

Star balanced carefully along the roof, her whiskers quivering with nerves. The only thing preventing her from losing her balance completely was her tail. Why did Moon enjoy this so much?

Moon was springing confidently from rooftop to rooftop. She looked as if she never wanted to stop, but Star certainly did. At least they were almost home.

Star sighed in relief as she leapt onto solid ground. She looked up at Moon from where she crouched. Moon nodded, and the two of them shuffled into a dark corner. Star peered around the lane, making sure that no one was watching.

Star and Moon shut their eyes. Pointed ears became rounder and lower on their heads. Eyes became larger, feline frames gradually grew bigger. Ebony fur slithered back into bodies.

Finally, there stood two human girls with long black hair. They smiled at each other and slipped through the back door.

Georgie Tiley (11)

An Attic Adventure

The door opened...

Out came a glowing waterfall and in the background, there was a forest full of glowing dragons and pandas. Then the glowing waterfall turned and twisted into a portal!

Stepping forward, I could smell the sweet scent of sugar and I could hear the flares from the dragon's mouth and the soft steps of the panda's paws. I could feel the breeze coming from the flapping of the dragon's wings and I could taste the mystery in the air.

Now, in front of me, I could see deserts, jungles, beautiful cherry blossom trees, lakes and volcanoes and every single one of my favourite animals was roaming in their natural habit. The trees were moving like something from Harry Potter.

All of a sudden, a mountain flew up out of the ground and I was stuck facing the wall of a cliff - it went up 200 million kilometres and the last 50 million were covered in thick snow (so deep that the tip of the mountain wasn't in fact rock but just very deep snow). Giant rock giants pulled themselves off of the cliff face, thinning the mountain. I could now see Avengers flying in from every direction. There was: Thor, Iron Man, Black Panther, Hulk, Captain America and every other Avenger you could imagine. Iron Man began to speak. He said, "In this world, every ten minutes will continue to change. There are five cycles, this is the second."

Immediately after he said it, the mountain collapsed! I fell backwards into a field of cotton candy; roaming in it was a tiny army of cute blue Stitches.

Owls flew in from the sky, as well as dogs. They landed on lollipop trees and settled on the candy cane grass. I lay there for a bit before everything began to swirl and change again.

An ocean appeared, full of dolphins, turtles and sharks, all living in a tranquil world. The dolphins began to play, splashing me as they did so, causing me to turn and see even more of the vast sea. There were strange-looking land creatures that had fins and gills allowing them to survive in the ocean. Suddenly, orcas appeared and as I looked away from them, I noticed that every other creature had vanished, and so too had the ocean...

Now I was standing on sand, next to a ginormous volcano spewing lava all over the desert. Fire pandas were protecting the volcano from the orcas we saw in the previous world. The orcas were attacking by shooting ice darts and bubble bombs. Few fire pandas were left but they were fighting hard and soon, help arrived for them - a Pokémon army. Together, as a pack, the orcas retreated to the lightning clouds above them.

As if by magic, I was swept off my feet and when I opened my eyes, I was sat, once again, before the attic door...

Jake Shayler (11)

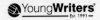
Ice Skating School

In 1984, there lived a girl called Lucy. She had three sisters. Their names were Ella, Lila and Coco and their big brother was called Gilbert, Bert for short. Lucy's mum and dad were also farmers. Ella was the eldest, her job was as a carer. Bert worked in a clothes store, Coco loved to cook well and Lila liked sport. Lucy loved ice skating. She did skating at school and she loved it.

A few weeks later at breakfast, she got a letter. It said: 'To Miss Lucy Norris, you have been invited to the Diamond Ice Skating School, signed Mrs Lewis'. She gasped in astonishment but decided to go. It was a boarding school which meant she could only come home at the weekend.

So, two days later, Lucy packed her suitcase, said goodbye and went on her way. The train journey was only 20 minutes but Lucy met a girl who went to Diamond Ice Skating School and they became friends. She was in the middle of a conversation when they reached the skating school. She was so nervous but soon forgot about it when she got to the rink.

When the lesson was finished, she got comfortable in her room and made friends with the other girls, Lily and Isabel. When Lucy went down to dinner, she met her teachers, Mr Jones, Mrs Lewis and Mr Thomas. Lucy liked them all. Mr Thomas was a bit strict but the others were nice.

A few weeks later, Lucy was training for a competition when she heard her teachers talking. They said it all depended on Lucy at the next competition. If she got onto the medals table, the club would be safe.

Lucy rushed into the room. "What do you mean? Why do I have to get a medal? Why is the club in danger?"

The teachers said, "Don't worry. What's happened is the club has run out of money but if you get a medal, the investor will give us money and the club will survive. This will mean everyone will be able to ice skate again, so practise and practise."

Over the next few days, Lucy worked so hard and on the day of the competition, she did her routine perfectly and got the gold medal. The investor decided to give the club money but that's not all. The man was called Tom and he decided to take Lucy to an ice skating school in Austria and he would take Lucy's mum, dad, three sisters, brother, dog called Bob, the chickens, horses, donkeys and don't forget the cow, Buttercup.

The next day, they left England and moved to Austria.

When they were on the plane, they played card games the whole flight. When they got to Austria, they moved into their new home and settled in. Lucy was so excited, she couldn't wait to get to her new ice skating school, but that's a story for another time.

Inyana Norris (10)

The Horrifying School Nightmare

It was a cold, misty winter and everyone was inside snug as a bug with fires on and windows closed. It was dark and all you could see outside was flashing bright headlights zooming around.

I wondered how my new school would be. What if people weren't nice or I did not fit in? What then? I was always homeschooled so I never knew what a public school was like. The only thing I can remember was when I was at nursery. I got paint all over me and everyone laughed. *Hopefully, it won't be like this*, I thought to myself. I whispered quietly to the window, letting a little fog on it. If only I could see the future that awaited me...

The next morning, I woke up and it was still raining heavily. Everyone was still inside their lit-up houses. But me, no, I had to go to school. Though, I couldn't say I wasn't excited. If people were friendly and kind I could fit in quite nicely, just like a jigsaw puzzle. If I could wish for anything, it would be to have friends. Yes, just to have friends.

I walked down the stairs to expect a nice warm welcome from Mum, but all I could see was a note on the table. It read, 'I left you money and warm clothes. I will be back soon XXX'. I grabbed the 200 and got my jacket. It was too tight - I didn't have money, nor the time to get a new one. I stumbled and tripped over because my jacket was so tight. When I tripped over, I reminded myself that I was going to a new school and just could not wait. I laughed and kept walking.

I finally got there but... it was so filthy. The walls had sticky spiderwebs and the wallpaper was peeling off. The classroom doors made a creaky sound and the shelf had books coated with dust. Mice crawled around the teacher's desk and not a single person was in sight.

I rushed to the principal's office - there was no one there and banana peels and crisp crumbs were on the floor. I tried to get out but my shoe stuck to a piece of bubblegum. I desperately needed to get out. I saw my life closing like a seashell, locked away in a... dirty school?

When I finally finished taking off the sticky gum, I ran... I ran and ran and ran and ran and ran and ran forever but it felt like I was not moving.

I puffed out of breath and started to walk home. I needed food but all there was in the shop was beans so I nibbled off some chocolate. I don't know why that school was dirty so I decided to go out the next morning. No one could stop me.

I came to the school the next day and saw children playing on the grass. I was so confused. What happened to the dirty school? I knew I was not crazy so I enrolled for the school... again.

Summer-Rose Campbell (10)

Moonlight Travesty

Crackle! the lightning went as I was in bed. My mum had just run to the shed to see what happened to the power. I slowly got up from my bed. The floor creaked, the whole room dark, the opposite of the sky outside. The sky was purple, that was strange! I went over to the window and saw it was raining, droplets overlapping one another. What was taking Mum so long? Although Mum specifically came to me and not my older brother and stated very clearly to stay in my bed, I grabbed my overcoat and slipped on my slippers. I creaked down the stairs. With each step I took came a loud creak. A rat scuttled into the kitchen. What had happened? The little fellas were ever so lively, they would scuttle around the house like it was theirs and as a matter of fact, they would do their stinky business in the cornflakes! What did they think the food was, the toilet? At least I did not see them on the actual toilet. What a sight that would be! They actually thought my other option of morning cereal would be Bran Flakes. That is what old people eat like my Aunt Peggy. She loves her morning Bran Flakes but I don't think the toilet does very much.

The door was wide open. I looked outside. The wind rushed in my face as the moon was complete. A howl came from nearby. Footprints led to the gates, too big to be Mum's and way too big to be a human's. I followed them to take a closer look. I turned behind me, the coast was clear but why did I think I felt a figure lurk behind me?

I heard Mum scream. I ran to go check. "MUM! ANSWER ME, PLEASE!" Tears ran down my cheek as I called out. No answer.

I ran to the shed to see the door closed. I picked up a shovel nearby and held it close to me. I kicked open the door to see Mum lying on the floor knocked out cold and blood dripping down her head. I fell to the ground on to my knees and checked if she was breathing. I looked in her pocket to see if there was anything that could help which there was not. Luckily I disobeyed her and found her here. I did not even think for a second. I ran into the house to go tell my brother. I climbed up the stairs to find his bed empty. I searched the house which was a workout. I grabbed the phone. 'No signal' read on it.

I went outside to look but then I fell to the ground. A mysterious animal, a wolf, I think, scratched my whole leg. It had glasses just like my brother. It was him. He then started chewing my leg, blood spewing everywhere. I screamed for dear life. No one heard. My heart stopped. *Boom!*

Hanan Abdi (11)

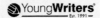

Don't Look Back

I heard a noise in the corridor, footsteps, and quickly got into bed, pretending to be asleep. I peeked above the covers and saw Mrs Lilian walking into our room. I held my breath waiting to see which person she would walk over to. To my horror, she began to creep towards my best friend's bed and she started to whisper a strange spell.

I'm Oliver. I'm fifteen years old and I'm here to tell you why you should never go to ThornWood hall. Anyway, as she was working her spell, I desperately tried to think of a way to stop her from finishing her spell. I knew I was one of her favourites but jumping up out of bed and trying to distract her might be pushing it. She was our foster mother after all. Maybe I should explain everything. I was very small when my mum and dad died in a plane crash and then Mrs Lilian started fostering. I have absolutely no idea why because she is a horrible, evil, deceitful woman and let me tell you why. Every time you make the slightest mistake or misbehave, she is there. She won't shout or whip you, but late at night when you're asleep, she will come into your room and start chanting a spell. If you're lucky, you will wake up with a splitting headache but if you're not lucky, well, let's just say you won't be feeling anything, and that was about to happen to my best friend ever.

Miles and I needed to help him. I did have some magic of my own but just the ordinary kind, just summoning mist and things like that, but how could I exploit that? Maybe I could summon some mist and hide us from view, then break out? That seemed like the best option, so I began to summon it. It felt so soft and cold, yet I knew how dangerous it was.

As the mist grew, I realised it was too late. It wasn't growing fast enough and only Miles would be able to leave if I weaved it in his direction. I jumped out of bed and whistled long and loud. Miles leapt from his bed in alarm as he realised what was happening. He ran with me towards the door. He tried the lock while I still summoned the mist so she couldn't see us.

"It's locked," he cursed.

"Let's try the window," I said.

I felt my energy draining from the strain of making the mist. We ran over but it too was locked.

"Let's just break it," I managed to mutter.

He picked up the closest thing: a shoe. He threw it at the window. We climbed out and ran into the freedom of midnight, never looking back.

Beatrix Blanco (10)

In The Sky

Sun:
Bright colours, orange and yellow
Sitting under you is a very happy fellow
Beams of heat
Warm up our bare feet
You shine down upon us
Make us happy in a taxi or a bus
You are the sun
Under you, it is always fun
Only clouds can block you out
And then it's always going to be a pout
You make grass thrive
And you help us watch out for beehives
With you, we can see
And peacefully drink our tea
If we went too close to you
We would die (and boil too!)

Snow:
You fall down in tiny flakes
Sometimes we put icing like you on birthday cakes
Together you make a great white rug
I like to lie down and give you a great big hug!
In your tiny little flakes
You settle in vast flowing lakes
When you are by my door

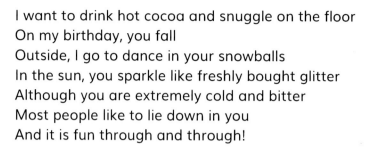

I want to drink hot cocoa and snuggle on the floor
On my birthday, you fall
Outside, I go to dance in your snowballs
In the sun, you sparkle like freshly bought glitter
Although you are extremely cold and bitter
Most people like to lie down in you
And it is fun through and through!

Rain:
You are extremely cold and wet
When you fall down, it is a struggle even to get to the vet
When the sky cries by the seaside
You get swallowed by the retreating tide
When you fall, all the animals enjoy your instant wash and
all your water
That prevents them from getting tauter and tauter
You can be tears of sadness or joy
People have different feelings about you whether they are a
girl or a boy
You give the smell of petrichor
That makes us wish for more and more!

Wind:
You are a strong breeze
And you blow away all the winter freeze
You carry the spring and summer flowers
From trees that are as tall as castle towers
You pick off leaves from the tallest trees
That fall to the ground green as peas

You can be a soft breeze or a strong hurricane
That will whip up the hairs on a horse's mane
When you're strong, leaves fall down
And land in the red fluffy hair of a circus clown
You rustle the trees
And blow away their leaves
You can fill canvas sails
Letting boats pass seals and whales
You blow our flying kites
And make them dance through days and nights.

Storm:
Your grey clouds fill the blue sky
And make the heavens cry
You make noise, loud and sharp
That will scare off salmon or carp
Blue, gold or green light
In a sky as dark as the middle of the night
One strike and we all want to go back to our home
You strike up the sea foam
You can make trees fall
We're in danger if we're tall
You scare the animals, small or big
And make trees rustle, oak or fig.

Omega Lambert-White (9)

My Holiday

Dear Diary,
I went on holiday to Mauritius by plane,
I went there to see Grandma and Grandad!
I saw my cousins in Mauritius.
We went to the seaside,
We went to lots of beaches,
And we went to a hotel to look around and have lunch there.
I went to stay there.
I went to a fun pool party with my cousins!
Everyone got in the van and went to the beach.
We got a boat and we went to a big beach.
On the big beach, we made sandcastles,
And had a picnic over there.
We then went on a long walk.
My holiday was over,
So I went back to England on Air Mauritius.

Meghna Boojhowon (7)

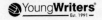

Tintin's Curious Adventure

Once upon a time, there was a family of badgers. There was Mummy Badger, Daddy Badger and Tintin.

One day, Tintin asked his parents if he could go and explore the world. His mum and dad thought it was time for him to go and explore, so they agreed.

Tintin ventured out and saw many interesting things. Somehow, he seemed lost! Where was he? There were speeding cars everywhere in every colour!

Suddenly, someone pushed him onto the road with a prickly paw! It was Timber the Hedgehog. Tintin had met Timber before and knew he wasn't nice. Luckily, a kind man went out of his way and took Tintin off the road.

Then suddenly, to Tintin's surprise, a mad German shepherd chased him all over town! His horrified owner couldn't catch him. Finally, after lots of running, the owner put the dog safely on the lead.

Tintin turned around and found himself by a group of flautists. A cat was nearby listening carefully. All of a sudden, the cat's eyes darted towards Tintin. It didn't look happy. The cat tried to swipe at him! Tintin ran away.

Soon, Tintin found himself at the local zoo. At least that's what a monster with a very long neck told him. The monster started dropping huge leaves on him, so he ran as fast as he could out of the zoo.

Tintin ran to the nearby local river he saw nearby. Suddenly, the river started to wash him away from shore. An otter nearby saw this and for a while, just watched. Then he decided to help the poor badger and put him on the bank.

Tintin didn't know where he was, so decided to lie down for a rest. Night fell and Tintin lay down to rest. Where was his family?

Suddenly, something swooped by. It was an owl. A wise owl. The owl asked, "What's the matter, young badger?"

"I'm lost and I've lost my family. Lots of animals are being really unfriendly towards me!" said Tintin.

The owl had heard of a missing badger, so he picked him up. While they were in the air, Tintin said, "Where are you taking me?"

The owl replied, "Home."

Finally, Tintin was home and had found his parents. His mum and dad tucked him into bed and said goodnight. While Tintin was in bed, he dreamed of all the animals he had seen, except a bit differently. There was a rose-red hedgehog, a German shepherd with rubber teeth, a very kind cat, a very short monster with a very short neck, an otter on land and a nice, kind, yellow owl.

Madison Bennett (9)

Joshua And Daniel

There once was a boy and his name was Joshua. He was disabled and really liked playing basketball at school; Joshua wanted to be an NBA player like LeBron James with his friend Daniel. Daniel played a lot of pranks, even though he knew it was bad.

One day, Joshua and the rest of the class had a substitute teacher since their teacher was not feeling well. The substitute teacher was named Mr Anderson. While Mr Anderson was teaching the class, Daniel tried to play the funniest prank ever on him. He asked to go to the toilet, but instead of going to the toilet, he went to look for a whoopee cushion. But he couldn't find one, so he secretly crept out of school and went to the corner shop to buy a whoopee cushion. Then he realised he hadn't brought any money because you were not allowed to bring money into school. So he decided to steal. He looked down all of the aisles and found a blue whoopee cushion. So he took it and ran back to the school. He went right into the gate and hit his nose and fell. Purple blood started gushing out of his nostrils. Since Daniel was taking so long and his teacher thought he had gone to the toilet, he went around the school looking for him. When he found him, he called an ambulance and told them what was happening. It turns out that Daniel was an alien. That meant Joshua had an alien friend. He tried to stay away but Daniel kept on getting closer and closer. Joshua didn't know what to do.

When Joshua got home from school, he told his family everything. He told his sister, Lyla, his mum and his dad, but they didn't believe him, they thought he was playing a prank on them.

When his mom dropped Joshua at school, she saw Daniel and he definitely looked like an alien, so she told the teacher to not make Joshua sit next to him in class, but since Mr Anderson was still teaching the class, Mrs Brown didn't know about them switching places.

In class, Daniel still tried to communicate with Joshua and it was so hard to ignore and stay away from him. In English, he tried to get his attention. Joshua couldn't do his work properly. At break time, Joshua saw Daniel sitting all by himself. He strolled up to him in his wheelchair.

"Are you okay?" asked Joshua.

Daniel sobbed. He didn't have anybody to play with him, so Joshua said sorry, and they played together.

Tamara-Mae Mwandira (8)

The Conspiracy Of The Cone

Pocket money, we were recently given,
The excitement in me was driven,
We decided to get summer food,
We would have been happy if not for one interlude.

So me and my sisters went straight to the market,
Though we had to be home before dark,
It was a house rule that we had to be back,
Before the sun went dark and came down with a whack.

So we got there,
And had a good stare,
We pondered on what to get,
Though you'll know this, I bet,
We decided to get ice cream!
For it's the best dessert ever seen.

My sister, Isla, got a nutty milkshake,
And that was what she saw them make,
Right in front of her eyes,
I felt the hunger in me begin to rise.

Eileen got a double scoop on a cone,
Though the ice cream was a slightly strange tone,
The ice cream was very black,
But hold up, this story has gone off track.

Finally! My turn to buy,
I looked around for what flavour to try,
I got very berry on a cone,
I felt that by then my hunger had grown.

We started walking back home,
Then my ice cream started to melt,
The scoop fell straight off the cone,
Sad was how I felt.

Isla offered me some of her drink,
But she hadn't stopped to think,
I am allergic to peanuts and oats,
If I had accepted, I'd have had a swollen throat.

Then Eileen offered me some of her ice cream,
It was the strangest scoop I'd ever seen,
The colour made it look disgusting,
But there's nothing to lose in trying a new thing.

I took a spoonful,
Feeling unsure,
But because of its taste,
My hunger started to thaw.

Back at the ice cream stall,
No one was buying there at all,
Now I'll tell you,
Why the ice cream slipped down,
When I learnt, I certainly had a frown.

The ice cream server,
Went to school with my dad,
They weren't the best of friends,
So to get revenge, she was very glad.

She had used,
Dark magic,
So that when I started to lick,
The ice cream fell to the ground,
And then I sadly frowned.

"How do you know this?"
You might ask,
Well, learning it was a task,
That I found quite easy
Like a click of a button,
1, 2, 3.

I own this thing,
That looks like a jewel,
It turned out to be,
Very useful.

It can detect bad magic so,
When that happens,
I will know.

So we swept on with our day,
Although there's one thing I'd like to say,
From now on, avoid that shop,
Then even her ice cream won't make me stop.

Flo Warman (9)

The Day Sea Dragon, Maximus, Was First Sighted

On a hot summer's day in Norway, a young girl called Storm was born. Her brown, creamy eyes, her brown, dusky skin, and her frizzy, long hair reflected her immense beauty. However, that's not all that came with the package. Also, she was very intelligent, a quality that became noticeable at a very young age - it started manifesting during her early years - but little did she know what her fate had in store for her.

By the time she was 12 years old, she could multiply eight-digit numbers together in less than a minute, and since birth, her beauty grew every day. Her skin was as bright as the sun.

She had a best friend called Nor and together they would go out into the woods to have adventures, create monsters, and find out how to destroy them. Wait! Doesn't that ring any bells?

One day in autumn, they came across a fjord curving its way around the mountain into the unknown... for all they could see. Their gaze shifted to the aquamarine river sea. Coming out of the fjord was a creature, a creature that had never been seen before. It was practically the 'Loch Ness Monster' that was last sighted in Scotland. This creature had never been seen in Norway.

Slowly, Storm and Nor's heads spun around to face each other. The first moment, they were gawking at this unimaginable sight. The next moment, they were sprinting back home to tell their mothers.

At home, they told their mothers all about it. Their mothers didn't believe them, so to prove their mothers wrong, they took them back to the fjord. Surprisingly, they bumped into each other at the crossroads. When they got there, the kids ran ahead to show them the creature, only to see the red clouded eyes of the creature go under the surface to survey the depths of the fjord.

When their mothers reached the fjord, they surveyed the surface of the fjord with the girls. "Now, now, girls! Galivanting around the woods has probably jumbled your brains," said their mothers as they walked back home.

Later in the week, there were reports of fewer fish in the fjord and yesterday there were reported sightings of a monster's silhouette. Therefore, Storm and Nor decided to do something about it. So they decided to go monster watching...

Esther Thompson (11)

How The Teddy Got Its Fur

I am a teddy bear, but not a normal one. For I am a magic teddy because I can walk and talk.

My owner was called Lavender, she snuggled me each night. She had long black hair with blue eyes. One night when she was snuggling me tighter than ever, I ran away. As like when all teddies come alive, my eyes started glowing. Then the next second I was alive.

When my owner woke up, I was gone. I was glad to get away from the stuffy bed. I was soon running down the garden path. Then I slipped. And there was no one to help me. I got myself up. Soon I was running again. It was getting dark. I saw a tawny owl. It was brown and black and white. Soon it was too dark to run. I was soon lying down in the soft grass. I got a large leaf. The owl I saw flew back to its hole.

When I woke up, I set off again. Then I saw a fox and it took me in its jaws. It took me to its den. The den was stuffy and smelly. Then I started wriggling and I just managed to get out. I shall never forget that moment.

I started to run again. Soon I saw a building. I went into the building. Then a person came along so I lay down as still as a statue. The person picked me up.

Then I noticed I was in a school.

If you want to know, a human is something we never run from. The human took me round the school. She asked if I was anyone's teddy. But of course, I was no one's. The girl asked if she could use me for the teddy bear drop and the teacher said yes.

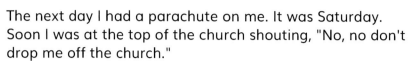

The next day I had a parachute on me. It was Saturday. Soon I was at the top of the church shouting, "No, no don't drop me off the church."

But it was too late.

After I was dropped off the church, I was very battered. After I was dropped off the church, I was taken to the person's home who made me the parachute. The person who made me a parachute was a friend of my owner. The person's teddies tried to hide me so I wouldn't go back. They wrapped me up in a rug.

But my owner found me, and she was very surprised. She tried to take the rug off me. But I wouldn't let her because it was so comfy and that is how teddies got their fur.

Lottie Seager (6)

Sky Land

Once there was a girl named Lily. She lived with her mum and her brother. One morning she woke up and heard her mum shout from downstairs, "It's time to wake up, Lily!"
"Why so early?" Lily replied.
"We're moving. Didn't I tell you?"
"No!" shouted Lily in anger.
"Well you have to get packed!" her mum shouted back.
So Lily got up and ready. First, she packed her clothes, then her other bits and bobs. Then it was time to leave. She wasn't happy about moving.
When they arrived, Lily went in first. She entered the house. All she could see was cobwebs hanging from the ceiling and doors leading to other rooms.
She went upstairs to see her new room. It was very dusty and there was a dead rat in the corner. "Aargh!" she screamed. The dead rat disgusted her. She unpacked her stuff. She opened the wardrobe in her room. She tripped up and fell into her wardrobe. *Bam!*
It was like she was on a different planet. It was so cloudy it seemed like she was up in the sky.
"Welcome to Sky Land," said a tiny little creature with wings.
"Who are you?" said Lily.
"My name is Gerry. I am a bubble."
"A bubble?" Lily replied.
"Bubbles are creatures that live up in the sky," he said.
"Oh," Lily said. "Well I really need to get back home!" Lily cried.

"Okay, okay, follow me," said Gerry.

So she followed him. On the way, Gerry was telling her about Sky Land and himself. "Do you know that every bubble has a different power?" he asked.

"No, of course not. I don't know anything about you," she replied.

"Oh yes, I forgot," said Gerry.

"Oh, here we are," Gerry told her.

"Finally," she sighed.

Then she was back home.

"Are you okay, Lily?" her mum shouted. "I have been looking for you everywhere."

"Oh I was under my bed covers taking a nap."

Ruby Muldoon (9)

Geo Quest: Jungle Mission 1

Crash! I got stuck in the vegetation and undergrowth of the Amazon Rainforest. My friend, Louis, helped me. I told him to open the earthy, fabric pocket bag strapped around my waist. I then told him to get a metal multi-tool and to use the silver, glistening blade to cut the vines to cut me free from the mossy, stubborn trees. *Slash!*

"Zain, are you okay?"

"Yes," I replied, weakly. I took the multi-tool and slotted it in my pocket bag and strapped it up. I noticed that twenty-five per cent of the squad was gone.

Suddenly, I saw a violet-pink spark flash past in the blitz of a second. I ran as fast as a golden and black spotted cheetah. I used my rough grappling hook on my harness to cling onto the rocky cliffs. I got out a disc from my bag... There was a hole in my disc holder to put data in about habitats.

"How did you know the data was on jungles?" Louis asked curiously.

"Because it had a leaf icon."

I told him I collected samples of moss, twigs, bark, roots, bugs, fur and more.

"Where are Max and Ronin?" I asked Louis.

"Dunno," he replied.

"Let's..."

"Ha!"

"Malvel?!"

"What are you doing here?" I asked.

"Destroying the world, *obviously!*"

Zain fought the dark sorcerer, Malvel, both backing up after every mistake; but in the end, Zain won the battle.

"I will get the power to destroy the plant with your disc..."

"Not if I can do something about it." *Slash!*

"Ronin!" I was relieved.

"Where's Max?" Louis demanded.

"He's in the unknown..."

"Guys!"

"Max!" I shouted. "Where were you?" I asked.

"No time to explain. We need to go through the portal but first..."

"Zain's saved the data!" Louis exclaimed.

Now we could take it back to the headquarters. One more step towards becoming heroes.

Eesa Gaffar (10)

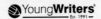

Our Queen

Way, way back in Edwardian times,
Elizabeth was born in the royal line.
Uncle Edward was the king when Cupid struck,
To marry Wallis Simpson, he was out of luck.

Abdicating from the throne to be with his love,
George VI wore the crown, the sceptre and the glove.
Elizabeth was growing into a fine young lady,
Princess of the Commonwealth when Europe was shady.

World War II filled the limelight as Elizabeth bloomed,
She drove a truck in the war when all seemed doomed.
April 1944 on her 18th birthday,
She was given a corgi who paved the way.

The dog, named Susan, set the royal line,
Of over 30 corgis in Elizabeth's time.
On her 21st, she made a promise she would keep,
To dedicate her life until her time to sleep.

She married her love and they toured side by side,
Making history in Kenya when King George VI died.
The 'most wonderful experience' with 'rhinos all night',
Elizabeth now Queen, as her dad lost his fight.

Embracing her role with grace and finesse,
Our Queen took the challenge and gave it her best.
Official engagements and opening the house,
With an annual address and her loyal spouse.

Her family grew and her parliaments changed,
Her son had a family and the heirs rearranged.
But our Queen led the country, through thick and through thin,
Always dressed to impress with a hat and a pin.

Her country, her family, she shared it all,
At weddings and funerals, she always stood tall.
An icon of Britain with the capital her home,
She travelled to Balmoral for her time alone.

Balmoral estate was her favourite castle,
She spent every summer there without any hassle.
This summer was different, its long lonely nights,
Protected our Queen, as she gave up her fight.

She kept every promise, right through to her end,
As she aged and she slowed, she maintained this trend.
She welcomed Prime Minister number 15,
Advised now, to rest, she is no longer seen.

The country in mourning, from D-Day -1,
The role of our royal passed on to her son.
'London Bridge' it's announced has fallen down,
Long live the King! Who now wears the crown.

Evangeline Ellery (11)

Night Howl

Chapter One: Silent

The wolves were sleeping but night fell. Alia and Evie were wolves.

Kaboom! The wolves flew up.

Evie and Alia went smack bang on the ground. "Ow!" they cried.

"Ha!" roared Laco the cat.

Josh, who was also a wolf, whispered to them, "Go!"

So off they went.

"Hey, Evie," said Alia, "we can go in."

"Okay," Evie agreed.

"Who goes there?" said a deep voice.

But Alia and Evie kept going. "Aargh!" they screamed.

"Oh sorry. Hehe, the name's Jacob. I'm a bear," he said. "Join me, if you want."

So they joined him.

"Let's go to the forest," Alia said.

"Huh," said Jacob.

"Wait," said Evie.

"What?" said a voice.

"Wait," said Evie.

"Huh," said Jacob.

Then dead silence fell. A gloomy shadow fell too.

"Um... Alia, is it just me or is Jacob gone and a shadow's above us?" Evie said.

Chapter Two: Boo!
"Boo!" Jacob went. "Haa ha ha!" he went. "You should have seen your faces."
Evie and Alia rolled their eyes. "Jacob!" they shouted.
"Sorry," he said.
So they kept walking and met a rabbit called Snowy.
"How ya doin', chaps?" he said. "Meet my sister, Fluffy."
"Oh hi," came a little voice. "It's me, Fluffy." A rabbit popped her head out from behind a tree.
"Do you want to join our team?" Alia, Evie and Jacob said.
"Yes!" they said.
"So let's go to Laco's castle, team!" said Alia.

Chapter Three: The End
"Guys, here we are, Laco's castle."
Off they went in the castle to Laco.
"Hey Laco, look at your team," said Alia and Evie so the battle began...
And they won! Laco was their friend.

Poppy Langridge (8)

A Witch Who Lost Her Wand

Once upon a time, a hundred years ago lived a witch. She was an old woman with grey hair, little legs and little arms. The witch had a hat, witch costume and purple shoes. She lived in a castle on an island. She was a good witch but she lost her magic wand. And she travelled all over the world to find it.

When the witch noticed that her magic wand was gone, she searched the whole castle but didn't find it. She thought she'd lost it when she travelled to the humans' kingdom. She decided to use a device which must find the wand. The device tracked the wand with trolls and two months later it was with the elves. The witch wanted it back.

She took her ship and went to the elves. These elves were very aggressive, and without asking her anything they greeted her with a war. But the witch won this war, because she was powerful, and defending killed a lot of elves. And only after this, the surviving elves asked her: "What do you need?"

"I need my magic wand," she answered.

"We don't have it," the King of Elves replied.

And the witch went to People's Kingdom. The king of this kingdom asked her: "What do you need, witch?"

"I need my magic wand back," she answered.

"We don't know where it is," the king said.

And the witch went back home with this bad news. But a thought came to her mind - *I haven't visited the trolls.* She took her ship again and swam to the trolls.

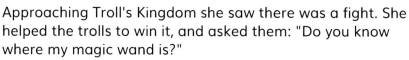

Approaching Troll's Kingdom she saw there was a fight. She helped the trolls to win it, and asked them: "Do you know where my magic wand is?"

"No," they replied.

She took a map to swim back home and realised she didn't swim to a small island which didn't belong to any kingdom she'd visited. She swam there and found her wand on a shore. She was so happy she found it, so singing a song about her magic wand she came back home happy and safely.

Anna Blazhko (9)

My Life Story

Ever since I turned six, my whole world went, let's say, like the life of a remarkable child. My sister was born, exams were coming up and I was about to go to a new dwelling. I still wished that I was a little girl, when studying and looks didn't matter. Anyways, after my Eleven Plus exam came, nearly my whole family were sick and school was getting harder and harder to cope with. The only things that made me happy were my ambitions. This is what I meant in short for 'This is me!'

My first passion began when my dad showed me his painting from 2000 to edit in 2020, a flower vase. Art. My best piece of art was made in August 2022. It was called 'Candy Girl'.

Walt Disney's quote: 'The way to get started is to quit talking and begin doing'. It inspired me to start my YT account (which also has 'Candy Girl' shown in a video). You can express anything you want with art, whether it's science, music or thoughts and feelings. Art also helps others to express themselves and make the world around them a better place.

Art comes from the heart and so does dance! When you dance, you show that you are brave, imaginative and loyal to make your dancing stunning from a soul of ecstasy. Dance is essentially emotion in motion. Yes, dance in its essence is about expressing the deep, guttural emotion that gets into the core of us.

To dance, you need music and miraculous singing - resulting in a sense of euphoria or relief and trust. Singing is a healer. You can say what you want to say but people will fathom it differently by using distinct body language and tone so you can sing your heart out.

To do everything in your own way, you need to have a brave and flourishing well-being to be successful in life. If you don't have happiness, you have nothing.
"Be unique in your own way,
Even if it means leaving things which are hard to forget."

Aditi Sikder (10)

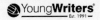

EI 777

We were the only ones left. I took my first step into the swirling mass of the portal, closed my eyes and shouted, "EI 777! EI 777! EI 777!"

In an instant, the hand of my mum disappeared from my shoulder as I shot through space at the speed of light...

Squelch! I had landed. On the damp, foggy ground. It felt as if it was quicksand. Glancing around, the first thing that my eyes were drawn to was the vibrating, yellow, smiling device implanted onto my arm. Written in welcoming bright neon letters was: 'Welcome to EI 777'.

Suddenly, a piercing sound burst my bubble of serenity. "Alert! Alert! Alert!" *That's weird.* My thoughts were interrupted as the sound, "Malfunction! Malfunction! Malfunction! Emergency chip activated!" screamed in my ears, amplifying each second.

Just as I saw it, in milliseconds, unconsciously, I was pulled aside, losing my balance, just in time before a levitating humanoid robot zoomed over my head. Phew! Without my emergency microchip, I would have been burnt toast!

Now, you might be wondering where I am - the new planet, which I was teleported to a few minutes ago. Our original habitat is overpopulated and a few million humans have volunteered to live here for the rest of eternity, it's now our new home. I had a feeling that it would be as safe as it ever could be! Due to nano fibres embedded into our clothing, we can safely explore! There are also sensors that automatically change the temperature of what we are wearing depending on our environment (EI 777 monitoring device). Danger instantly subsides, so dangers like black holes or comets can't ever enter the atmosphere - the magnetic field around our planet is immensely strong; dangers in space simply bounce back into the oblivion of the universe. Wait... Where did that humanoid robot go? And where is everyone?

Azra Eva Yavas (11)

There's A Dragon In My School!

I'm just a normal boy, living a normal life - until the new boy came, Harrison.

He wore a green striped top, a black and blue hoodie and grey jeans. He had red hair and a baseball cap. He didn't look like he should be in primary school because he towered over all the others and even looked older.

The next day, we both went to breakfast club. Harrison drew a detailed picture of a dragon, he was really good at drawing! Then he told me to take a look in his bag and went to get it. Inside there was a giant, red, mischievous, fire-breathing DRAGON!

Harrison said, "This is my new pet I found on the way to school. He hasn't got a name yet but we need to feed him first before he breathes fire and turns us into dust."

So we fed it toast, which got burnt when he coughed, and Rice Krispies (well, he ate all the crispies in one go so tried the box and I don't think he enjoyed it) until Harrison's bag ripped and the dragon was HUGE and too big for toast and cereal so he ate the fattest dinner nanny we've got.

He looked satisfied with his meal and shared a look with us as if to say 'can we come here again tomorrow?'

We decided he needed a name so we called him Jeremy Dragonite Fisher, or 'Fisher' for short.

The other kids were starting to come into school so we attempted to hide Fisher under our coats and went to maths class. It was so boring that Fisher even fell asleep!

When we finally went out to play Fisher was flying us over the basketball hoops and even toasted some marshmallows that the older kids had sneaked in.

At last, it was lunch and Fisher went for SCHOOL DINNERS! They thought he was a human and luckily gave him the chicken. I don't even believe it but everyone thinks he's a student!

I just can't wait for tomorrow with my new two friends!

Oliver Bayat (9)

The Monster Of The Seas

"Dad, can you tell me the story of the brave dog, please?" asked the little boy. "Of course, my child," said his father. "A few weeks after Aquaticalizon was defeated, Gizmo (an aquatic robot dog) was told to go and defeat Bloug, the blob monster. So Gizmo, being the good dog he was, went to defeat Bloug. It was a treacherous journey since Bloug's castle was across the sea.

Eventually, Gizmo got to the castle, but it was barren of life. There were cobwebs framing the door and a crown was lying lopsided on the red carpet. Gizmo walked slowly forward and saw two wooden doors parallel to each other. Gizmo decided to come back later after he found Bloug and defeated it.

When Gizmo got to Narvale, the town was in bits and pieces. Just then, Gizmo saw a blob-like thing that seemed to be the size of a skyscraper (or at least half the size of one). Gizmo knew it must have been Bloug.

Bloug turned around and looked at Gizmo and started getting closer. Bloug picked a house that was mostly intact and threw it at Gizmo.

Gizmo just barely missed the crash. Gizmo tried to attack Bloug with a stick but it absorbed into Bloug. Bloug picked up a piece of the ground and threw it at Gizmo but missed again! The dust got into its eyes so Gizmo threw a piece of metal at Bloug which hurt it. Gizmo then threw another much bigger piece of metal which hit Bloug in the stomach and made Bloug fall over and get knocked out.

Gizmo had defeated Bloug.

Gizmo went round Narvale and found all the people who lived there but they didn't have anywhere to live. Gizmo suggested that they should clean up Bloug's castle and live there. Everyone agreed (well except Bloug)."
"What happened next, Dad?" asked the little boy.
"Maybe next time," said the father.

Nathan Arnold (9)

This Is Me!

My name is Zanna,
I am a beautiful African princess from Nigeria.
Let me tell you about my heritage.

C ommunity and togetherness are what we value
O ne big and loving family is everybody
M ummy told me that about my heritage
M y background includes friends that
U nderstand the value of friendship
N obody is ever alone or lonely
I am so proud of my African roots
T his is my heritage too
Y ou should be proud of yours too.

G reetings are important in my heritage
R espect is always expected
E very child should not call any adult by name
E very adult looks after all the children
T here is no difference between families
I was told to call adults uncles and aunties
N one of them were my family members but
G reeting elders that way shows respect.

F ashion is what we like
A rtistic designs
S tylish gowns
H airstyles that look like crowns
I like the dresses Mummy makes for me
O r the brightly coloured beads for my hair
N ice, nice, nice, they all look

M usic is part of my heritage
U sually, it goes with dance
S ome dancers are male and some are female
I love to sing and dance too
C ause music makes me happy always.

F ood from my heritage is yummy, so yummy, mmm!
O h, if you taste Mummy's jollof rice, you'll agree
O r the okro soup that I love to eat and
D rink Supermalt, the yummy Nigerian drink.

This is me.
My name is Zanna,
The beautiful African princess from Nigeria.

Zanna Orunsolu (6)

A Trip To The Safari Park

On Wednesday morning during the summer holidays, we packed some snacks and got in the car. We were ready to go on a trip to the safari park.

When we arrived, it was very cloudy, so we got on the coach and put on our seat belts. We said the prayer for safety and the coach set off to the safari park. On our way, the boss took the register. When we arrived at the safari park, we got off the coach and went to the toilets.

After we were done, we got back on the coach to have a tour inside. First, we saw the rhinos. They were enormous! Then we saw the deer and giraffes. Suddenly, a giraffe was about to lick the window. After that, I saw a sign that said: 'White lions and tigers'. We saw a lion and tigers. Me and my grandad saw reindeer, goats and an elephant. Then we got off the coach.

When we got off the coach, I rushed to the rides. I went on a caterpillar roller coaster. I even went and pretended to be a fire shooter. As soon as I got off the ride, it poured heavily, so we quickly rushed to the reptile house. In the reptile house, we saw an orange frog and a big snake in the water. When the rain stopped, we hurried to a toy shop and there, I bought a soft artificial penguin and a toy egg that hatched in three days. After we came out of the shop, we went to get some ice cream!

While I was enjoying my delicious strawberry ice cream, my grandad was having his late afternoon tea and biscuits. Suddenly, an announcement was made as it was time to pack up and leave. We quickly finished our ice cream and tea and headed towards the coach.

We boarded the coach, and the register was done. As soon as the driver started driving, I fell asleep as I was extremely exhausted. Overall, it was a fantastic trip and I enjoyed it.

Rayan Shah (7)

A Handful Of Sand

Once in a mammoth hotel, lived a sweet, young girl. Her name was Honey and she was 8 years old. She loved drawing, painting, colouring and travelling around the humongous natural world.

Today, Honey was packing up her suitcase because she was going to Egypt. "YAY! I can't wait!" shouted Honey. She got into the car and drove to the closest airport. When she got on the plane, she fell asleep.

When she woke up, she was jumping up and down until she was tired (maximum 2 hours). She rapidly stepped off the plane onto the dry, hot sand.

Later she went outside to play. She took a handful of sand and vanished. Honey looked around and realised that she was in a pyramid. Suddenly, she saw two old, dirty doors. She went through the second one because she had a feeling that nothing would happen.

Out of nowhere, arrows were flying above her head because she stepped on a trap that was hidden on the long floor. On the walls, she saw a sticking-out brick that caused a fire. So, Honey didn't touch anything and looked down not to step on anything.

Honey saw a cup of water on the ground but little did she know that it was a trap. A massive stone fell on her arm but gladly she was alright. So even if there was something tempting, she didn't dare to touch it.

She finally went to the end. There was a big tomb. It was the tomb of King Tutankhamun. She heard that it was cursed so she ran to the light. It wasn't guiding her to a safe exit but the alternate universe.

She was in a different world made out of shapes. She was scared because she had trypophobia (the fear of shapes). The door shut behind her. The legend says that if you come in there you will never come out. Honey was stuck in there forever.

Pola Dworak (9)

The Detention

Everyone forgot my best friend, including me, then they forgot me. This is how it all happened. A kid called Ricky Witherman copied my test answers during maths and claimed that I copied his answers. I, of course, denied everything. It still didn't change the fact that we both ended up in detention.

Now about Ricky Witherman. Every single person, even his parents, called him Repulsive Ricky. They called him that because he always had to blow his nose, sometimes he did it into his sleeves or even into other children's sleeves!

Suddenly, in the middle of our detention, Repulsive Ricky stood up and waved his arm in front of the security camera. There was some mysterious smoke filling the room around us. I realised that the security camera had disappeared and absolutely no one could see what he was about to do. No one but me.

I was about to leave the classroom when Repulsive Ricky quickly waved his arm at the door which locked immediately. He started speaking in a language that I didn't understand. A bright violet light then started glowing all around us. The door was unlocked and I came out. Nobody saw me or remembered me.

Surprisingly, I started to remember my best friend. He was with Repulsive Ricky before I completely forgot him. Then I saw him and he saw me. Together, we escaped school. Suddenly, a man wearing black came out of nowhere...

We couldn't see his face as it was covered by a black mask. He was waving a sharp sword around like a maniac. He got him killed... My best friend was dead. All alone I was.

I walked around to see Repulsive Ricky was dead too. Now no one could be with me. The only person I was with was he who killed my best friend.

Nellie Gustaw (8)

Death Has Charged In

Could they ever be happier?

Architectural sandcastles startled crabs with their natural beauty; soft beams of light cast a glittering glow upon them, making it seem as if you could step inside.

Laughter spilt out across the beach - everyone's faces lit up with broad grins.

Whilst the salty sea air filtered through their noses, they frolicked across the sand, collecting pristine seashells.

What was happening?

The laughter died down and was replaced by a gasping silence.

The seashells cascaded from their hands, scattering and cracking. Sandcastles collapsed, their beauty fading. The sky morphed into a macabre grey at a sickeningly quick pace. Danger was coming.

Were they going to survive?

Rumbling, pounding, burning; darkness extinguished all good thoughts and memories.

As they reached the place that they had believed was safe, they were truly heartbroken. Their whole lives were crumbling before their very eyes.

Flames like hissing snakes slithered their way up monumental buildings, demolishing all hope and good spirit.

Howling sirens and spluttering coughs were all they could hear, dust and smoke engulfing them in a painful fog.

Sprinting away from terror, gasping, wailing, crying. But their father wasn't a match for the darkness.

It bared its teeth, then carelessly ripped him away from his family, never to be seen by his loved ones again.

Death has charged in.

Daisy Northfield (11)

South Africa

South Africa is the home of apples, cool right?
South Africa is a wonderful place where people also make food from scratch like pap. Pap is almost like rice but very tasty in the country's opinion.

Did you know?
The first heart transplant was in South Africa in 1967.
South Africa has eleven official languages including Afrikaans, English, Xhosa, Zulu, Southern Sotho, Northern Sotho, Tsonga, Ndebele and Swati.
South Africa has landmarks like Table Mountain, Mount Kilimanjaro, Victoria Falls, Okavango Delta, Olduvai Gorge, Aloba Arch, Zuma Rocks and Avenue of the Baobabs.

South Africa has the big five: lions, elephants, black rhinoceroses, buffalos and leopards.

South Africa is a country in southern Africa. It's famous for the food, culture and landmarks. 84.2% of South Africans are Christian. Don't leave South Africa without eating... boerewors, Cape Malay curry, Malva pudding, chakalaka and pap, braai shisha, nyama or bunny chow.
It has a subtropical climate. It is the largest producer of macadamia nuts in the world! There are more than 2,000 shipwrecks on the South African coast. It's famous for being the largest producer of platinum and the world's fourth-largest producer of diamonds.

Cool Facts:
South Africa is very hot and in winter it's not really cold.
South Africa has Table Mountain which is a mountain that's flat like a table.
South Africa has really nice beaches and very pretty cities.

Zoe Da Paixão (10)

Reboot! 1, 2, 3, 4...

Chorus:
Reboot!
Reboot!
Reboot, ooh!

Bridge:
Reboot, you got to reboot!
Reboot, you got to reboot!
Try changing your boots, so you can reshoot,
You got to reboot, ooh!

Verse one: (rap)
'Cause I stay in my house just like a small mouse,
And Covid is on the case, now we've got to stay based.
Boris Johnson is the one,
Something's got to be done.
We don't wanna stay home, we wanna have fun!
Marcus Rashford took us kids off mute,
That's when the football made its great shoot.
Now Covid has gone (root-a-toot)
The best thing you can do is just reboot!

Bridge:
Reboot, you got to reboot!
Reboot, you got to reboot!
Reboot, you got to reboot!
Reboot, you got to... reboot!

Verse two: (rap)
Social media can be a bug,
Crawling like a slug.
But don't let it send you up the wall,
What's the sense of it all?
If you feel stressed or not the best,
Just walk away and make the most of your day.
Get away from the pressure and get ahead,
Put the infection on mute,
The cure is to just reboot!

Bridge:
Reboot, you got to reboot!
Reboot, you got to reboot!
Reboot, you got to reboot!
Reboot, you got to... reboot!

Chorus:
Reboot!
Reboot!
Reboot!
Reboot - boot - boot - boot - boot!

Leo Obe (9)

Life That You Wish For

Woah oh, woah oh, woah oh, oh, oh
You open up your eyes to a new big surprise
A world that's waiting for you yeah, ay, aye
I've never really seen such a thing before
But it takes my breath away listening along...
Sometimes life is not what it is about, woah oh
You keep movin' higher and higher
Ahhh woah, yeah, ohhhh ah
You keep on dreaming like there's something waiting for
you, ooo
Yeah, ay, ay, aye, yeah, ay, woah oh
You never really knew how strong I was
But tonight I stand and sing as loud...
As loud as I want tonight...
I just want to sing the world
Alright, the world is shouting my name...
This is the power
'Cos baby, I just want to feel
Live my life as long as I want
I am gonna say it out loud... as loud
This is the power
You came looking for, woah ohh oh
This is something better than you wanted to know
Something you wanted to remember all the time
Woah ohh oh
This is the power

You came looking for, woah ohh oh
This is the power everybody's coming for, yeah, yeah, yeah
Try and stop me now, what u comin' for,
Woah, oh... yeah, yeah... ahh
Try and stop me now, what u comin' for,
Woah, oh... yeah, yeah... ahh
I am gonna say it out loud...
Maybe I didn't see it then,
But now I scream to say that I want to...
I just want to be myself
As long as everything stays the same,
Woah, oh, oh, oh
Yeah, yeahhh, aye.

Amina Kanwal (11)

The Blitz

The terrible and tragic Blitz in World War Two,
Gave us an almighty hint - an essential clue.
That Adolf Hitler was cold-hearted,
When the dropping of bombs started.

Petrified, melancholic children were sent away,
In their new homes and families, they began to pray.
Alarms wailing, citizens running,
Confusion, chaos, machines gunning.

Distraught people huddled close together,
These would be the moments they would treasure forever.
The warning siren ensured and made us certain,
To close all of our swaying, open curtains.

Thousands of bodies lying on the streets,
Our brave, courageous army accomplishing extraordinary feats.
Buildings in ruins, rubble scattered everywhere,
A sense of lament yet pride in the air.

The end of the terrible bombing brought great relief,
And banished misery and some of the grief.
The spirit of them all unbroken,
Words like loss, never spoken.

Today there is no conflict and bloodshed,
Everyone everywhere is cared for and fed.
Now we live in a country that's serene,
Was this real or was it a dream?

Aarush Garg (11)

I Am A Fish

I am a fish in a pot.
How I wish to sail.
My pot is small and the world is wide.
I want to be under the sea.
I wish to see an aeroplane or an aero-train.
I wish to see a race car, I want it to race.
I can swim to the glass, really, really hard.
Yes! It's moving!
I am tired. I will not give up.
Aaaaaargh!
I am falling off the table.
I am on the floor, but still in the pot.
I can see the door, but I can't open it in my pot.
Oh, look! Someone is opening the door.
Yes, I am outside!
The house is near the beach.
It's just a short road away.
I am on the sand, but still in a pot.
My pot is nearly in the sea.
I have to dodge the seagulls.
Good, I dodged all the seagulls and I am in the sea.
But I am still in a pot.
I think I am going to bash the lid.
Look! It is my mum.

She is helping me.
Thank you, Mum.
We are best friends forever.

Aaron Shaw (5)

A Quest Through Ancient Egypt

As the stifling sun rose over the translucent clouds, the air became arid. It felt like I had been journeying for miles. The distant cawing of the birds was ferocious. The insatiable thirst was painful. I stopped for a break and turned around to see a gargantuan pyramid. I entered cautiously. Venturing deeper, I spotted a statue. The jewels that glistened resembled someone of importance. Perhaps royalty. In that moment its eyes awoke staring straight through me

A boom echoed around the room. A huge boulder blocked the exit. I stood lifeless as it slowly approached me. Will I escape?

Aaryan Acharya

Summer Sonnet

There's a gentle breeze flowing through the trees
And it feels like summer is here today
New flowers are here, listen to the bees
Look at the summer water in the bay

The weather is warm and the sun shines bright
It rains a lot but is always so hot
In summer, the days are long and light
The stars and the moon glitter a lot

We get lots of new birds tweeting loudly
Lambs grow up bigger and calves grow up too
Out in the hills, the stags stand up proudly
I love the summer as much as you do

Late summer turns into early autumn
We give the new season a warm welcome.

Mia Martin (8)

God's Good Earth

God's good Earth,
Always having new births.
Peace all around the world,
With miracles being performed by Jesus.
On God's good Earth.

God's good Earth,
Jesus has had to rebirth.
There is lots of fun for lots of children,
In lots of theme parks and with toys like Lego.
On God's good Earth.

God's good Earth,
Everything has worth.
Soon to be destroyed,
Replaced by another.
On God's good Earth,
On God's good Earth,
On God's good Earth.

Tristan Meacher (9)

Queen Elizabeth II

Her Majesty the Queen
With her smile so bright
With her legacy, she lit a path of light
With the help of God and the right people by her side
She was a woman in whose trust we could abide

Through 15 Prime Ministers
Even though she started as an artificer
She was Queen of 15 countries
And had her face on most of the currencies
Canada, New Zealand, Australia and the United Kingdom
Even though these are just some
She led them all with a keen eye and wisdom

Oh, Her Majesty the Queen
Your memory will never cease
Rest in peace.

'Nehita Aigbogun (11)

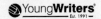

The Little Mouse

Once upon a time, there was a little mouse called Buttercup. The mouse met the big bad wolf, and Buttercup was terrified. So, she ran away - but the big bad wolf was only trying to help her get home, so he followed her around. The wolf lost track of the mouse, but he found her again eventually, and they became best friends. Until the wolf killed her! But she was only faking it, so when the wolf's back was turned, she went up to him and stabbed him in the back. He then fell to the ground dramatically and died.

Meredith Ivy Caunt (6)

Yuki

Yuki was born on a floating island. Ever since the day he was born, he hated his parents because they treated him like a dirty sock. Sometimes he saw them dispose of his pets and make up stories about their disposal.

One day, Yuki had had enough and tried to fight his parents but he failed and got banished to the underworld which was usually called Earth. He found Earth fun and he got an idea. He went to school and graduated from college. Then he started to make a machine to stop his parents from doing harm...

Jaafar Aouam (11)

The Queen

T he Queen reigned from 1952-2022.

H eir to the throne in 1950, but two years later, after her father, King George VI, died, she became queen.

E lizabeth reigned for 70 years.

Q ueens have been violent in the past, but this one was different.

U nited most of the world's countries and the Commonwealth.

E lizabeth did so many things in her time.

E lizabeth will be greatly missed.

N ever leaves our hearts.

Ethan Lawry (10)

A Letter To God

Dear God,

Thank you for today and for all the things you have done for us.

Thank you for protecting us through the time of Coronavirus until now.

Thank you for providing us with a wonderful world.

I feel happy for all the love you have shown to me.

I love you so much, God.

I will sing praises to you, day and night.

I will also pray, day and night.

I will share your word of hope and love to many people.

Thank you, God!

With love from Gifty xx

Gifty-Favour Thompson (9)

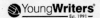
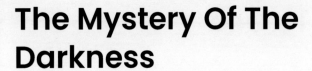

The Mystery Of The Darkness

It was getting dark. I had to find Mollie before it was too late. Before the unthinkable could happen. Before the whispers came out of the shadows and pulled me in like a dark hand grabbing me from behind. Before the fog engulfed the moonlit sky. Before the path ahead faded into complete darkness.

For a moment I stopped to listen to the leaves rustling in the trees. Then I heard it. The distinct sound of footsteps pacing behind me. I wasn't alone!

Kaylan Merrell (11)

Teacher And Fairy

T　eachers are like best friends
E　very day they are with me
A　re very welcoming and smile at me
C　alm faces when I come in
H　ard work being at school
E　veryone does good, indeed
R　eady to learn, ready to compete.

F　amous fairies
A　mazing creatures
I　nteresting and playful
R　ainbow dresses
Y　ellow, golden hair.

Dulcine-Vittoria Dubceac (6)

Poem For The Queen

We thank you for your years of service
From young queen to old
You have been through so much with us
I know, and what I have been told.

From a war to a pandemic
From births to deaths
You held your head high
You are our own Lillibet.

Please now rest in peace
And reunite with loved ones
Your name will never be forgotten
For many years to come.

RIP, Your Majesty.

Ciena Baldwin (11)

The Titanic

There once was an iceberg,
There once was a ship,
The ship was called the Titanic.
It was to sail across the Atlantic.

The owner cried, "It's gigantic,
Indestructible and dynamic!"
However, the iceberg had struck,
The passengers were prisoners: stuck.
Everyone was out of luck.

The Titanic had been impaled,
Its one clear mission had failed.
The unsinkable theories were astray,
But the legend continues to live today.

Sophia Clayton (11)

The Beach

When I go to this place,
It puts a smile on my face.
The sand sparkles like golden jewels,
I love exploring in the rock pools.
The sea gently calls my name,
Wanting to play that wave jumping game.
The sandcastles I made,
With my bucket and spade.
Glistening water coming to me,
Dancing waves I can see.
The sparkling sun that goes down,
As I return to my town.

Olivia Finch (10)

The Rainbow

When I woke up one morning
And looked at the sky
The day was rainy and sunny
At the same time.
I spotted seven colours
Appear in the sky:
Red, orange, yellow, green, blue, indigo and violet
Caught my eye.
The rainbow in the sky
Was shiny and bright.
I wondered, was there a pot of gold nearby?

Anjali Ramalingam (7)

The Cat's Eyes

Can you see the winking
Then blinking
Sinking?
Then a noise of meow
Just now
Then a shuffling sound
On the ground...

Green eyes peering
Seeing and fearing
It has a tail
That looks like a sail

I know that creature on the mat...

It's a cat!

Marni Allcorn (8)

Rainbow

A rainbow...
Is as red as my favourite colour.
Is as orange as the autumn leaves that I kick.
Is as yellow as my daddy's lentil dahl.
Is as green as Green Lantern who is fearless.
Is as blue as the end of my day.
Is as purple as my mum's favourite colour.
Is as black as my PSP.

George Frank Gamble (9)

Drops Of Rain

Drops of rain,
It could be harsh enough for pain,
Fast or slow,
You might see a rainbow,
Don't think it's boring,
Because it can sound like snoring,
You could have fun,
But the sad part is that it could be done,
So when it rains, go out and play,
Even during May.

Haasika Vishnuprabhu (9)

Sandwich

S andwiches everywhere are very tasty
A nd I love lettuce and cheese on mine
N ever forget the butter
D o remember to half it
W hen you are ready, take a bite
I t tastes so good
C lean away your mess
H ave you made a sandwich before?

Oliver Thompson (7)

Superhero

He is as fast as a cheetah.
He can jump like a frog.
He is as strong as a tiger.
He is as loyal as Superman.
He can fly like a bee.
He is as brave as love.
He can leap as high as the wind
And he is as tall as a tree.

Fred Gamble (7)

Superhero Rules

Have a big heart
Do the right thing
Save princesses
Have a bright smile
Love your family
Save the day
Always do your best
Have big dreams
Be yourself and
Never give up ever, ever!

Shakeel Gariba (4)

Joshua

J osh loves chocolate cake
O ften I have pudding
S uper Sonic is my favourite
H ome is the best
U p into the air, I want to go there
A nd fly around the world.

Joshua Madders (5)

Emotion Mystery

I smell like strong vinegar,
I taste like a bitter apple,
I look like a storm's clouds,
I sound like a puff of smoke coming out of a train,
I feel prickly like a hedgehog,
What am I?

Answer: Jealousy.

Josie Meech (9)

Space

S olar system
P lanets orbit the sun
A stronauts are 'space sailors'
C omets have tails
E arth has one moon.

Arun Dutt (5)

Thank you for reading this Young Writers' Annual Showcase anthology!

We hope that you enjoyed it. When creating the Annual Showcase anthologies, we felt the best approach was to categorise entries by age due to some of the themes tackled by older writers. Anthologies therefore contain either 4-12 year-olds or 12 and over entrants. We do encourage young writers to express themselves and address subjects that matter to them, which sometimes means writing about sensitive or contentious topics.

If you have been affected by any issues raised in this book, details on where to find help can be found at: **www.youngwriters.co.uk/info/other/contact-lines.**

YOUNG WRITERS INFORMATION

We hope you have enjoyed reading this book – and that you will continue to in the coming years.

If you're a young writer who enjoys reading and creative writing, or the parent of an enthusiastic poet or story writer, do visit our website **www.youngwriters.co.uk**. Here you will find free competitions, workshops and games, as well as recommended reads, a poetry glossary and our blog. There's lots to keep budding writers motivated to write!

If you would like to order further copies of this book, or any of our other titles, then please give us a call or order via your online account.

Young Writers
Remus House
Coltsfoot Drive
Peterborough
PE2 9BF
(01733) 890066
info@youngwriters.co.uk

Join in the conversation!
Tips, news, giveaways and much more!

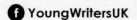 **YoungWritersUK** 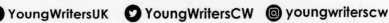 **YoungWritersCW** 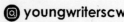 **youngwriterscw**